The Aromantic Guide to making your own Natural Skin, Hair and Body Care products

Kolbjørn Borseth

Precaution

The information published here is not intended as a substitute for personal medical advice. Before making any decision regarding your personal health, please consult a GP, Medical Herbalist, qualified Aromatherapist, other qualified health practitioner or a recommended reference book before using Herbs, Essential Oils or Absolutes. Pregnant women, the elderly, those with skin sensitivities or problems, or those with difficult medical conditions should be particularly careful when taking herbs internally, or when applying the Herbs, Essential Oils, Absolutes and other raw materials externally. It's a good idea to let your GP, Medical Herbalist, Qualified Aromatherapist or Health Practitioner know that you are considering the use of Herbs or Essential Oils as some may cross-react with conventional drugs you are, or may be considering, taking. Report any side-effects to your personal Health Care Practitioner.

Disclaimer

This information is provided for our customers and is obtained from a variety of sources, including the research, knowledge and experience of Kolbjorn Borseth. While we have obviously done our utmost to provide correct information, there may be errors.

USA: These statements have not been evaluated by the Food and Drug Administration (FDA). These products are not intended to diagnose, treat, cure, or prevent any disease.

17 Tytler Street, Forres, Moray, Scotland, IV36 1EL
Tel: +44 (0)1309 696900 Fax: +44 (0)1309 696911
E-mail: info@aromantic.co.uk
Website: www.aromantic.co.uk
© Copyright 2009, Aromantic
ISBN No: 978-0-9554323-1-6

Welcome

Welcome to the updated and expanded Revised Third Edition of *Aromantic Guide to making your own Skin, Hair and Body Care products*. The Guide has a brand new, much asked for chapter on Making Anti-Aging and Skin Rejuvenation Products.

I'm very proud to share with you the result of many years of work and dedication. Originally from Norway, I have 27 years of experience in complementary health and had the pleasure of opening my first natural cosmetics manufacturing company in Sweden 24 years ago. After working in Sweden, often in partnership with leading complementary health experts, I decided that I wanted to reveal the secrets of the cosmetics industry to both professional therapists and lay people. This Guide is one of the ways I share this knowledge. Apart from our series of Guides, Aromantic offers this information in a number of other ways: Educational Courses, Recipe Brochures, Newsletters and our website.

After learning everything you need to know about making these popular, natural products, you can then purchase all of the raw materials and equipment you require from Aromantic. We have strong ethical and environmentally friendly policies and endeavour to source the finest quality natural raw materials.

We are constantly improving the quality of what we offer and we hope you enjoy this edition of the Guide and the opportunities it offers to you to make your own Natural Skin, Hair and Oral Hygiene Care products. While I recommend that you attend an Aromantic Education course, this Guide is packed with information, recipes and step-by-step methods so that you can make your own natural, tailor-made products, whether for your friends, family or therapy clients.

Aromantic's mission is:

• to reveal to you the secrets of how natural cosmetics & skin care products are made professionally.

• to empower you to make your own products, specific to your own tastes and skin care needs, from home - affordably, ethically and naturally.

• to offer you the opportunity to start your own successful business, making and selling natural cosmetics, bath, hair or skin care products.

• to help aromatherapists, salon owners, beauticians and other therapists to tailor-make natural cosmetics specific to their clients' needs. We have a wide range of different raw materials that you can use to make products for certain skin and hair conditions and types, such as essential oils, vegetable oils, vitamins, minerals, anti-aging and other active ingredients suited to your clients. This is bespoke cosmetology.

• to provide our customers with the most up-to-date natural raw materials and information as soon as it is possible.

• to constantly search out, demand and consequently supply more organic raw materials such as essential oils, vegetables oils and herbs. This will encourage more growers to produce organic produce and to be more ecologically aware.

• through our work, to help as many people as possible with their different skin conditions and skin problems.

• to support, encourage and give advice to developers of organic raw materials and actives. Aromantic will always naturally be at the forefront of natural/organic skin care progress.

Acknowledgements

I would like to thank Finn Andersen of Crearome in Sweden, who started me out on this journey, when I attended one of his early courses in Stockholm in the mid-1980s.

To Lilly Johansson, with whom I worked for 10 years in Scandinavia, where she was a health icon. Over 30, 000 patients attended her state-funded alternative hospital, Follingegaarden, over a period of 30 years, from the mid-1960s.

To my wife Helena, and my family, who understand that for me teaching and sharing this knowledge is not a hobby, or even work…but a mission.

To all my loyal and hard-working colleagues at Aromantic, who have always supported me, with special thanks to my 'right-hand' here at Aromantic, Monika Dachs.

To Susan Kemp, who is getting good at reading my mind! Thank you for your excellent editing, rewriting and proofreading work on this Guide and my other publications.

And last but not least, to my customers. Many of you are my friends; all of you have inspired me to develop this knowledge further.

Enjoy the adventure!

Kolbjørn Borseth, Founder of Aromantic

Contents

Our Policy on Raw Materials

Our Policy on Raw Materials is based on a holistic perspective, which considers these in relation to nature and to people. Aromantic constantly monitors the market in innovative raw materials for Natural Skin Care products and Cosmetics that are the best for you as well as the best for the Planet in the long term.

Most importantly, we wish, through the information contained in this Guide, and other Leaflets, Brochures, Newsletters, our website and our Courses to describe exactly what our products contain and how they should be used, so that you will be able to make informed choices about Raw Materials based on our standards, other people's and your own. Raw Materials of the best quality are then selected in line with the company's overall ethos and according to the following criteria:

• Our aim is to sell Raw Materials, which are as environmentally friendly and as natural as possible. Raw Materials should come from renewable sources and through their life cycle (production, processing, use and disposal) should not damage or pollute the environment.

• It should be possible to classify and identify all Raw Materials according to their botanical (Latin) name, plant family, part(s) used, country of origin, method of cultivation, method of extraction and any other processes as well as the formal INCI declaration.

• To the extent that they can be obtained, and are of interest to our customers, it is our aim to sell as many Natural Raw Materials as possible that are cultivated without artificial fertilisers, chemicals and pesticides. We wish to support suppliers who promote organic methods and culture.

• We will not sell Raw Materials made from animal sources, e.g. slaughterhouse by-products such as gelatine, collagen, and animal-based emulsifiers and soap ingredients. These are by far the most commonly used materials in the cosmetic industry and we want no part of that. The only animal by-product we stock is beeswax and no bees were harmed in the harvesting of this natural product.

• We do not support the testing of Raw Materials for cosmetics on animals.

• Where we are unable to source Raw Materials which are not tested on animals we use Raw Materials that are at least guaranteed not tested on animals after 1996, thereby operating a fixed cut-off date system.

• Our aim is to avoid selling Raw Materials or related products derived from the petroleum industry (non-renewable source) e.g. products containing Paraffin Oil and Ethylene.

• We only sell Raw Materials that are synthetically produced where the natural equivalent would be derived from animals such as with Vitamin A or which cannot be naturally produced such as Preservatives and some Colours. The only exceptions to this are where the Natural Raw Material is very expensive and the cost cannot be justified by the extent of its use such as with Allantoin.

• We monitor all of our Raw Materials through the use of batch numbers, which enable us to trace them internally within the business from the point of delivery, through storage, documentation, product information and analysis and externally through to our customers and retailers. This is important to ensure the correct information is given and in the following up of any customer queries.

Aromantic is certified by Organic Farmers & Growers 2009

In May 2009, Organic Farmers & Growers Ltd informed us at Aromantic that we have been successful in our bid for organic certification.

Who are Organic Farmers & Growers Ltd?

Organic Farmers & Growers Ltd (OF&G) is one of a number of control bodies accredited by Defra and is approved to inspect organic production and processing in the UK.

OF&G has its national headquarters in Shrewsbury, Shropshire, and operates across Great Britain and Northern Ireland, as well as the Isle of Man and the Channel Islands.

As a leader in organic certification for well over a decade, Organic Farmers & Growers has turned its expertise in organic inspection and licensing to this sector and has developed its Cosmetic and Bodycare Standard.

This standard is based on the EU Organic Regulation (EC2092/91) and the Nordic Ecolabelling Standards.

What Aromantic's organic status means to you

You can be confident that the organic raw materials you purchase from Aromantic are indeed organic. It is unfortunate that many raw materials used in the cosmetic and beauty industry are marketed as organic when in fact they are not. More and more consumers are demanding beauty products which are free from harmful chemicals and that have not been genetically modified and Aromantic fully supports this. Aromantic is committed to purchasing organic raw materials wherever possible.

Under EU rules you can call your health and beauty products organic if the product contains organic ingredients. This does not mean that your products are "certified" as organic because your company has to go through the certification process because this process is also about your production methods, packing, distribution, etc and not just about the ingredients.

If your company decides to go through the process of certification, then the main advantage of Aromantic being certified organic is that you can be absolutely sure that you are getting truly organic products and if you go for certification yourself, then you will have Aromantic's organic certificate to prove that the ingredients you are using are really organic.

Another advantage to you is that you will be now using certified organic ingredients and can show Aromantic's certificate to prove it. Aromantic's Certificate of Compliance is available for downloading from our website.

Sensitivity & Allergy Tests on Raw Materials

It is impossible to create Skin Care products which everyone will tolerate, particularly in view of the fact that people's sensitivity have increased. Through testing Raw Materials and Ready-Made Products on the area of skin in the crook of the elbow – where the skin is thinner and more sensitive – you'll be able to determine whether or not you are likely to have an allergic response to what you have applied. This, of course, can be done with any product you purchase and it is particularly important to do this with anything you intend to use on your face.

How to test yourself for an Allergy

Choose an area in the crook of your elbow of a few square centimetres and apply the product or raw material you wish to test. Leave for 12-24 hours and then look for any signs of allergic reaction. The test may even be repeated the next day. Signs of an allergic reaction include red, warm skin, perhaps also itchy and/or with a rash. When testing raw materials it is advisable to test quantities in proportion to how they will occur in the finished product. So, for example, to test a Preservative, it should be diluted in water in a ratio of 0.5ml-1ml to 100ml water.

Essential Oils, Absolutes and Manipulated Oils

Essential Oils

Essential Oils are volatile, aromatic substances, which have a long tradition of use in natural medicine, perfume, incense, skin and health care. Using the Essential Oils of plants for therapeutic purposes is known as Aromatherapy and has been practised for thousands of years.

Essential Oils are mostly produced in three ways:

1) Water/steam distillation from seeds, roots, wood, leaves and flowers. This is the most common method.

2) Pressing of the peel of citrus fruits. Citrus Oils are the only ones produced in this way. These can also be produced through distillation.

3) Supercritical CO_2 Extraction is becoming popular now for producing Essential Oils. The advantage of CO_2 Essential Oils is really in their purity as this extraction method provides a high level of the active constituents of an Oil, and as so has a much cleaner and purer aroma and improved therapeutic benefits.

Extraction through the use of Solvents is a method also used for certain Oils. We do not call these Essential Oils as they do not contain true aromatic substances such as Absolutes and Resinoids but contain substances which are not volatile.

Absolutes

The delicate nature of many flowers means that steam distillation, the usual method of making Essential Oils, cannot be used to extract the Oil because the intense heat destroys the flowers, causing them to become compacted into a solid mass that the steam cannot penetrate.

Therefore, a special process using solvents has been developed to capture the more delicate fragrance without causing any damage to the fragrance. This process does not use any heat or water so none of the water-soluble aromatic compounds are lost the way they are in steam distillation. When an Oil is extracted this way, it is referred to as an Absolute rather than an Essential Oil.

Diluted Essential Oils and Absolutes

Some of the Essential Oils and Absolutes that Aromantic stock are diluted in either alcohol or Vegetable Oil. This is because some Absolutes or Essential Oils, such as Rose or Jasmine, are very concentrated and have an overpowering aroma. Just one drop in a pot of Cream can be too much. They are also very expensive, so diluting them makes these high quality Absolutes more affordable for you too.

Manipulated Oils

The trade in Essential Oils over the past 100 to 200 years has modified its product to suit its customers – the perfume, cosmetics, pharmaceutical, confectionery and food industries, tailoring it to what they require. Examples of this are: Lavender Oil, which smells the same year after year; Peppermint Oil with the same menthol content year after year; and perfumes, which require standardised ingredients. Low prices and standardised products have become more important than quality – but not to Aromantic.

This means that many of the Essential Oils on the market today are Manipulated Oils, produced by mixing Oils from different plant sources or by mixing Oils with synthetically produced aromatic chemicals. These Oils may be good for the purpose for which they were made – to provide a pleasant fragrance or aroma. You should be aware that many of these oils are sold under the guise of being genuine Essential Oils derived from a particular plant and therefore with particular therapeutic properties. This is simply not true and they will not have any of the desired effects of a genuine Essential Oil. In fact, if sold and used in this way, they may even do more damage than good. Rest assured that Aromantic takes the quality of its Essential Oils as an utmost priority.

Aromantic's Purchasing & Sales Policy for Essential Oils and Absolutes

Our policy is to sell 100% genuine Essential Oils of good quality, extracted from raw plants and parts of plants.

We are able to identify their chemical constituents, indicate whether or not they have been altered, manipulated, or contain only a part of the original Oil (as can happen with for example, Ylang Ylang and Camphor Oils). We are also able to indicate methods of growing and country of origin – all those details which you, the consumer, may require in order to feel secure in your choice of us as your supplier of Essential Oils.

We have chosen our suppliers of our Essential Oils very carefully. We work in close co-operation with different producers of high quality Oils from France and other European countries, as well dealing with small and fair trade projects in Africa and India. Whether producers or distributors, or both, our suppliers all share the following codes of Best Practice:

• Our suppliers are either the producer themselves and/or are a distributor who buys direct from producers all over the world. Through building up this direct contact with smaller growers and producers, whose methods are documented carefully, either the distributors, or we at Aromantic, are able to guarantee where the Oils come from, what growing methods have been used, how the Oils have been produced as well as how they have been stored.

• Before purchasing Oils, our distributors are provided with batch samples. These are tested for fragrance, appearance and consistency and the best one from amongst those that can be sourced to a defined plant or plant part is selected. When purchasing Organic Oils, all documentation is checked. If they are in any doubt about the Oil's constituents, a sample is sent to the laboratory for analysis. Aromantic is supplied with extensive and detailed Quality Test and

Analysis Data from our suppliers who are also the producers.

• When the Oil either arrives at the distributor or is ready for sale at the producer, it is given a batch number, which will remain the same and be recorded throughout their tests and controls. At Aromantic, we continue this traceability with our own system of linking suppliers' batch numbers to specific products that we stock.

• Our suppliers who are distributors also carry out their own quality control of all Essential Oils they buy in and do not solely rely on what the data the producers have given them.

How our suppliers carry out the Analysis of Essential Oils and Absolutes

There are several methods for ascertaining whether or not Essential Oils are genuine i.e. that they are truly volatile Essential Oils extracted from raw plants. Some of these methods make use of the physical senses. The fragrance of an Essential Oil will indicate its age, and comparisons are carried out with other samples of Oils of the same type. Do they smell the same? Are they volatile to the same degree? Do they smell synthetic? Do they smell of alcohol? The ability to detect the subtle differences through smell is acquired only with experience and training over a long period of time.

Different Essential Oils have different colours and consistencies, which can be seen and felt. An Essential Oil can be tested on a piece of paper to see whether or not it has been diluted with a Vegetable Oil: an Essential Oil is volatile (which a Vegetable Oil is not) and will not leave an oil stain (which a Vegetable Oil will). Anyone working with Essential Oils can learn how

to do this. The simplest physical tests, which are carried out are those that determine the degree of optical distortion the Oil creates, its refraction index and density.

Tests are carried out which combine gas chromatography with mass spectrometry: one separates the molecules in the Oil and determines how many there are; the other establishes what chemical constituents are present. The Oil is then assessed based on these tests and by studying data gathered from hundreds of other tests carried out on samples of the same type of Oil. Are the constituents comparable and typical? Are the different samples similar? There will often be a similarity between two out of three samples. In this way one can determine whether or not the Oil has been extracted from a raw plant and other Essential Oils, artificial fragrances or cheaper, isolated constituents of Oils have been added.

Please see our current catalogue or website for more specific about each Essential Oil and Absolute that we sell.

Safety & Storage Information for Essential Oils and Absolutes

Warning! Essentials Oils and Absolutes contain the active ingredients of a plant in highly concentrated form i.e. small amounts of Essential Oils are capable of huge effects. To obtain best results, it is important to use them correctly and sensibly. Overdosing can cause health problems! They MUST NOT come into direct contact with mucous membranes or, of course, with the eyes. Do not use Essential Oils undiluted directly on the skin and do not take internally unless advised by a professional. Essential Oils should be kept in a dark, cool place, out of reach of children and away from medicines. We recommend that you learn about the uses and effects/possible side-effects of Essential Oils before using them yourself and Aromantic do offer further Training Courses to help you.

Certain Oils should be used with extra care – please see our current Catalogue and our website for more detailed information.

Vegetable Oils, Fats and Waxes

Methods of Extraction

Vegetable Oils, Fats & Waxes are extracted from nuts, seeds, fruits, leaves, as well as bees in the case of beeswax. Extraction involving simple pressing in small oil presses has now been replaced by large industrial operations, which involve sophisticated methods and equipment and which now supply us, the shops and the cosmetics industry with these raw materials and nourishing ingredients.

There are several ways of producing Oils & Fats:

Boiling

Used primarily for the extraction of animal fats such as lard and tallow. Aromantic does not stock any animal fats.

Solvent extraction

Seeds or nuts are crushed and mixed with a solvent (e.g. Hexane) which 'draws out' the Oil. The Oil then undergoes several stages of refinement to remove the solvent and other ingredients present in the seeds or nuts. Heat is not necessary for the process. This is a very common method and is used to extract Rapeseed Oil as it yields a large quantity of Oil.

Hot pressing

Seeds, nuts and fruit pulp are crushed and heated and the Oil pressed out. This gives a larger quantity of Oil than Cold pressing does.

Cold pressing

Seeds, nuts and fruit pulp are crushed and pressed. Although external heat is not applied, heat is generated through the friction involved in the pressing. This is our preferred source of Vegetable Oils.

Supercritical CO_2 fluid extraction:

Supercritical CO_2 fluid extraction is becoming more and more popular as the intention is to eliminate harmful organic solvents used in the past for the production of lipophilic (fat-loving) Botanical Extracts, to avoid environmental pollution and to have a high grade extract composition very close to the natural raw material. CO_2 Extracts are much more pure and in a concentrated form. They are free of any solvent residues and diluting agents and are composed almost exclusively of the raw material's ingredients without any dilution and accordingly can be used in a fairly low dosage. This low dosage means that a high quality, active cosmetic product can be created at a reduced cost. **Note:** Although at Aromantic, we categorise products that that have been extracted in this way as Botanical CO_2 Extracts, one could say that they are Vegetable Oils, but with more of their active constituents intact, so much more concentrated and powerful. This affects their price and use i.e. you wouldn't use 100ml of Botanical CO_2 Extract for Massage Oil – you would only need to put a maximum of 3ml of the Extract into 100ml of a Carrier Oil that has been extracted by a more traditional, therefore cheaper, method.

See Table 1 opposite for a better understanding of some commonly used Oils, Fats & Waxes.

Table 1: Oils, Fats & Waxes

	Wax & Fatty Alcohols	Saturated Fatty Acids	Mono-unsaturated Fatty Acids (also called Omega 9)	Polyunsaturated Fatty Acids (also called Omega 3) & Duo-unsaturated Fatty Acids (also called Omega 6)*
Vegetable Oil or Fat	Beeswax, Carnauba Wax, Cetyl Alcohol.	Avocado Butter, Cocoa Butter, Coconut Butter, Mango Butter, Palm Kernel Oil, Shea Butter.	Apricot Kernel Oil, Avocado Oil, Castor Oil, Hazel Nut Oil, Jojoba Oil, Macadamia Nut Oil, Olive Oil, Papaya Seed Oil, Peach Kernel Oil, Peanut Oil, Sesame Oil, Shea Butter Oil, Sunflower Oil (High Oleic Acid content).	Blackseed Oil, Borage Oil, Camelina Oil, Chia Seed Oil, Evening Primrose Oil, Hemp Seed Oil, Kiwi Seed Oil, Passionflower Oil, Pumpkin Seed Oil, Red Raspberry Oil, Rosehip Oil, Sunflower Oil, Thistle Oil, Walnut Oil.
Consistency	Firm, hard & waxy (some).	Firm.	Liquid-thick.	Liquid.
Feel on the skin	Fatty & waxy.	Fatty & soft.	Semi-fatty.	Dry to fatty.
Absorption by the skin	Not absorbed by the skin. Creates a protective barrier on the top layer of the skin.	Takes a long time for the skin to absorb.	Slow absorption that offers good lubrication for Massage.	Easily & quickly. absorbed by the skin.
Shelf life	5-10yrs	2-5 years	2-4 years	1-3 years
Uses	Protects; gives consistency & stability to Ointments, Lotions, Lip Balms & Creams.	Protects, nourishes & softens; helps Massage products to glide over skin. Used in Ointments, Lip Balms, Creams and Lotions.	Protects, nourishes & softens; Helps Ointments, Lip Balms, Creams, Lotions and Massage Oils to glide over skin. (Particularly excellent for adding lubrication qualities to Massage Oils.)	Softens & nourishes; contains active constituents similar to Vitamins. Used in products, which should be absorbed deeply; and to render products less fatty.
How to store	Dark and Room Temperature.	Dark & Cool.	Dark & Cool.	Dark and Refrigerated.

Also collectively known as Vitamin F.

About Double Boilers/Bain-maries

When we refer to a double boiler, or a bain-marie, we are referring to a cooking vessel consisting of two nested pans, designed to allow slow, even cooking or heating of ingredients in the upper pan, without scorching or denaturing, by the action of water boiling in the lower pan. It is very important that the water in the lower half of the double boiler is actually boiling – this will ensure that the ingredients in the upper pan or bowl will melt successfully. You can improvise a double boiler, if you don't already have one – with two saucepans or a saucepan at the bottom and an ovenproof or stainless steel bowl at the top. It is not essential to buy specialist equipment if you are making products for your own pleasure.

Preservatives dosage guidelines for the Recipes in this Guide

The Recipes in this Guide contain dosages for Preservatives that are appropriate for Parabens (usually 10 drops/0.5%) or Preservative 12 (usually 12 drops/0.6%). Remember that Preservative 12 will not work in a product that contains Detergent. If you are using Preservative K, then increase the dosage from 10 to 18 drops (also see Moisturisers and Preservatives on pages 20 & 21 for more information about how to use this Preservative correctly).

Preservatives & products containing Herbal Infusions

You need to double the amount of Preservative in your product when you substitute Herbal Infusions for Boiling Spring Water in Recipes that contain Boiling Spring Water. This is because Herbal Infusions naturally contain a lot of bacteria and fungi.

An Introduction to making your own Creams and Cosmetics

In this chapter we will look at the basics of making your own Creams, give an overview of some of the more commonly used Vegetable Oils, Moisturisers and Preservatives used in making Creams and other Natural Skin Care products. This chapter can be referred to as you move on through the Guide and try your hand at making other products.

> Making your own Creams
>
> Vegetable Oils
>
> Moisturisers & Preservative

Making your own Creams

As you will have gathered, any Cream consists of many different ingredients which, depending on how these interact with each other, create a particular effect. Some ingredients are essential, such as a Vegetable Oil, or give Creams their consistency, such as Emulsifiers, while other ingredients are added for their cosmetic or healing effects on skin, such as CO_2 Extracts.

In order to be able to mix a Cream, all that is required is the ability to read a recipe and to weigh and measure ingredients accurately. Composing and creating your own Creams requires more knowledge and experience. Some knowledge is acquired through the process of following recipes and trying the results out on one's own skin. Any of the theory that one might require about raw materials, Herbs or Essential Oils can be acquired through reading relevant books. All of this information is equally important. See *The Aromantic Guide to the use of Herbs in Skin, Hair and Health Care* products for detailed information on how to use herbs in your products.

Creating your own Cream Recipe

The following description of how to plan your own recipe can be used as a guide to help you get creative. Begin by considering what the Cream is needed for. What sort of Cream will it be - for which skin type or skin problem? Let's say we want to make a Cream for dry, sensitive skin, which is easily irritated. Is there a main ingredient or Herb that should dominate the Cream?

Chamomile is an excellent Herb to treat this sort of skin type. In order to gain the maximum benefit of all of the active ingredients in Chamomile it is best to use an Infusion (soaked for 1-12 hours), Chamomile CO_2 Extract or Essential Oil of Chamomile or maybe even all three: the Infusion, the CO_2 Extract and the Essential Oil. For sensitive skin we recommend Apricot Kernel Oil.

Sensitive skin will also benefit from nourishment and vitamins that can help strengthen the skin. For this purpose, one would add Avocado Oil and undiluted Vitamin E Oil. Shea Butter is added to give the Cream a smooth texture. As dry skin needs moisture, one would also add NFF Moisturiser, which promotes moisture retention in the deeper layers of the skin. When you've selected the main ingredients, then the next stage is to mix the Cream. Always work to a Recipe that will give you 100ml/g once everything has been mixed together. This will make it easier to measure the ingredients (i.e. 1ml/g = 1%).

Start with the Fat Stage. How much fat should there be? Your Cream will be fattier or oilier the more you make at this stage in relation to the rest. The Cream in our example is for dry, sensitive skin, which is deficient in fats so for this one choose a Fat Stage amounting to 35% (i.e. 35ml/g of the total 100ml/g will consist of Fats, Oils and oil-soluble Vitamins).

The last item to calculate is the amount of water. In our example we are going to use water infused with Chamomile flowers. The Infusion in this case will need to be 62ml as the rest of the ingredients amount to 35ml but you actually start out the infusion process with up to double the amount of water (130ml) as some of the water will be evaporated and some will be absorbed by the dried flowers. **Note:** the amount of Preservative will be increased, as we are using a Herbal Infusion, and not just water.

Base Cream Recipe

- **Fat Stage (75-80°C)**

10ml Avocado Oil

9ml Apricot Kernel Oil

3g Shea Butter

2g Cetyl Alcohol

3g VE Emulsifier

- **Water Stage (75-80°C)**

4.5g MF Emulsifier

62ml Water infused with Chamomile flowers

20-22 drops (1ml/g) Preservative

- **Third Stage (40-35°C)**

1ml/g Chamomile CO_2 Extract

2ml/g Vitamin E Oil (undiluted)

3ml NFF Moisturiser

- **Fourth Stage (30-25°C)**

Essential Oils (8 drops of Roman Chamomile, 8 drops of Lavender, 4 drops of Bergamot or Mandarin - these Oils are added to enhance the Cream's fragrance and effect).

NB! If using Preservative K as your Preservative, make sure that the end product's pH is under 5.5 as Preservative K will not work if the pH is over 5.5. This is necessary to do for any product containing Preservative K. See pages 20 & 21 for more information. For Basic Method for making all Creams, see page 26.

Basic Tips and Suggestions for Making Creams

• If the Oil you use feels more "oily", the resulting Cream will also feel more oily. Also, the more Oil, of whatever type, that you add, the oilier the Cream will feel. If more water is added, the Cream will feel less greasy.

• The more solid fatty ingredients you add like Cetyl Alcohol, Beeswax, Cocoa Butter or Shea Butter), the harder the Cream will be. Without these solid fats most Creams would be liquid or milky.

• Weigh and measure all the ingredients carefully. If making up larger quantities than specified in the Recipe, calculate quantities for all ingredients thoroughly and write these down.

• Always use a double boiler for heating cosmetics at the Fat Stage. Then you will be able to ensure that the temperature never rises above 100°C. Hot Oil is flammable and can cause serious skin damage if you get it on your own skin. If the water in the larger pan boils away, add more.

Note: It is difficult to measure small quantities under 5ml/g accurately. To ease this problem it helps to multiply the Recipe.

How to rectify common mistakes when making Creams

Water or Oil separates from the Cream

This can arise through careless mixing of the Fat and Water Stages or one of the Stages may not have been beaten thoroughly enough or may have been made at the wrong temperature. The Cream may also have cooled too quickly, or not been stirred to room temperature. Perhaps you left the Cream to go and do something else? Try warming the Cream again to 75°C and, after placing the pan or heat-proof bowl containing the Cream in a hot water bath, whisk for 5 minutes, and then remove the bowl from the hot water bath, and allow to cool whilst still stirring it.

Cream is too hard

Too many solid fatty ingredients have been added or perhaps inaccurately measured. Adjust the other ingredients so that the proportions comply with the Recipe, or stir in cold water, adding a little bit at a time, and continue stirring until the Cream has reached the right consistency.

Cream is too thin

Not enough of the solid fatty ingredients have been added. The Fat and Water Stages may have been mixed too quickly, or the Cream may have cooled too quickly as a result of poor beating technique. Too little Emulsifier may have been added or may even have been forgotten. Sometimes the Stages can get mixed together in the wrong order e.g. Water into the Fat Stage instead of the other way around. The wrong ingredients may have been added at the wrong stage e.g. NFF during the Water Stage. Try warming the Cream again to 75°C and then whisk the mixture for 5 minutes. Allow it to cool down. If your original measurements were correct, then your Cream should now be thicker.

Cream is grainy

The Fats, Wax and Emulsifier have not melted and dissolved properly. Can be caused when temperature differences between ingredients are too great at the point at which they are mixed. Make sure the MF Emulsifier is mixed well with the water (especially around the edges). If there is Lactic Acid in the product this may have been added too early. Use an electric stick blender and see if you can dissolve the graininess or, if that doesn't succeed, try warming the Cream again to 75°C and stir for 5 minutes in hot water bath and then allow to cool while continuing to whisk the mixture.

Vegetable Oils and Fats for Health & Skin Care products

For thousands of years humankind has used Vegetable Oils and Fats in health and skin care and for massage. Different Oils and Fats have been used, depending on where people lived, e.g. Olive and Sweet Almond Oils in Southern Europe, Shea Butter and Coconut Butter in West Africa and Sesame Oil in India.

It has been, and still is, natural to use these Oils as they protect the skin, keep it soft and supple and help it to remain strong, healthy and beautiful. All Vegetable Oils nourish, soften and protect the skin.

As a result of the increase in trade between different countries we now have access to many different Oils and can choose which one to use, depending on the need, skin type and skin problem involved.

This is a brief introduction to the most common ones. See Aromantic's website for more Publications and also for free information in our Natural Skin Care Library.

Commonly used Fats and Oils

Apricot Kernel Oil (extracted from the kernel of Prunus armeniaca)
A mild Oil which most people are able to use. It is a softening and stable oil, which is especially good for dry, mature and sensitive skin. The Oil is semi-fatty and is easily absorbed by the skin. (Peach Kernel Oil has similar properties).

Avocado Oil (extracted from the dried fruit pulp of Persea gratissima)
Avocado Oil is a mild, nourishing, semi-fatty Oil, rich in Vitamins; Carotene (provitamin A), Vitamins B5 (Pantothenic Acid), D and E. It also contains Fatty Acids, Phytosterols, and Lecithin. Avocado Oil is used when the skin is dry, tired and lacklustre. It can be used in Face, Skin and Massage Oils. A good Treatment Oil for injured or damaged skin.

Blackseed Oil (extracted from seeds of Nigella sativa)
The main benefits of Blackseed Oil are that it is an anti-inflammatory. High in Omega 6 Fatty Acids, the Oil can be used in the treatment of eczema and psoriasis and it also has skin softening and anti-aging benefits. Blackseed Oil can be used in Lip Balms, Face Creams and Lotions, Healing Creams, Eczema and Psoriasis Products, After-Sun Products and in Soaps. The suggested dosage is 1–10% in Lotions and Creams.

Borage Oil (Starflower Oil) (extracted from the tiny seeds of Borago officinalis)
This is a very unusual Oil with its high content of Gamma Linolenic Acid (GLA), a substance the body needs to create prostaglandins. Borage Oil has similar properties to Evening Primrose Oil but contains 20-24% GLA compared with Evening Primrose Oil, which only contains 8-12%.

Prostaglandins are needed by the skin in order for it to function properly. Prostaglandin deficiency affects the skin's suppleness and will cause it to age more quickly, become more sensitive to light and to become dry and wrinkled more easily. Borage Oil can be added to other blends of Oil in a concentration of 5-30%. Eczema and psoriasis respond well to Borage and Evening Primrose Oils.

Castor Oil (extracted from the seeds of Ricinus communis)

Is very fatty and thick and is very slowly absorbed by the skin. Good for Lip Balms, Cleansing Creams and Massage Oils. Add up to 10%. It adds shine to Lipsticks. Castor Oil makes very good cold processed Soap and also makes the Soap transparent. A stable Oil which does not easily go rancid.

Chia Seed Oil (extracted from seeds of Salvia hispanica)

Chia Seed Oil is a thin, dry and very soft Oil, with a silky soft skin feeling & a pleasant smell. It has a very similar Omega 3 & 6 content to Kiwi Seed Oil, but is much cheaper to buy (about one-third less at the time of writing). It soothes fine wrinkles and improves skin elasticity, so add the Oil to Serums, Creams and Lotions for these purposes. It is good for treating acne-prone, oily and large-pored skin and as it is so silky & soft, it is excellent for sensitive skin too.

Coconut Butter (extracted from Cocos nucifera)

Extracted from the inner layer of the Coconut shell. It remains solid at room temperature but melts easily when in contact with the skin. It is traditionally used as Hair Oil but has also been used as a Sun Oil. Another use for Coconut Butter in Skin and Massage Oils is that it makes them slightly thicker or fattier and also prevents them from being absorbed too quickly by the skin.

Evening Primrose Oil (extracted from the seeds of Oenothera biennis)

For properties and uses, see Borage Oil.

Hemp Seed Oil (extracted from the seeds of Cannabis sativa)

Apart from its excellent cleansing and moisturising properties, Hemp Seed Oil is unique in its make up and rivals Oils such as Flax Seed Oil as a dietary supplement. Hemp Seed Oil has a well-balanced ration of 3:1 of Omega 6 and 3 Essential Fatty Acids respectively. It is the presence of these Essential Fatty Acids in this particular ratio that helps improve skin conditions such as eczema, psoriasis and acne.

It is also a rich source of Gamma Linolenic Acid (GLA), the main valued content of Borage and Evening Primrose Oils, which is believed to help premenstrual tension (PMT), menopause and arthritis. Hemp Seed Oil may also benefit other inflammatory diseases such as rheumatoid arthritis, osteoporosis, Crohn's disease and ulcerative colitis. Hemp Oil is a very dry and mild Oil and is good for normal to oily skin.

Jojoba Oil (extracted from the seeds of Simmondsia chinensis)

Actually a Liquid Wax, but known as Jojoba Oil, has been used for hundreds of years by the American Indians. Provides slightly more cover or protection as it contains wax-like substances. It softens, protects and helps the skin to hold its moisture. It contains a natural Sun Protection Factor of 4. Also good as a Hair Oil for e.g. Dandruff. It is good for all skin types and especially for conditions such as acne and dry eczema. It will keep for 4 to 5 years without going rancid.

Kiwi Seed Oil (extracted from seeds of Actinidia deliciosa)

An unique Oil as it contains a very high level of Omega 3 Fatty Acids (up to 65%) and other micronutrients. Skin studies have shown that it improves skin condition & protects against moisture loss. The Oil has an excellent after-feel and absorbs easily making it the perfect ingredient in Face Creams and Hair Conditioning Creams. Being so soft and smooth, it is also suitable for sensitive skin.

Macadamia Nut Oil (extracted from the kernel of Macadamia tetraphylla)

A fatty Oil, which is soft and nice to use. Despite its fattiness, it is readily absorbed by the skin. It is especially good to use for mature and dry skin as well as skin which has difficulty retaining its moisture.

Olive Oil (extracted from the fruit of Olea europea)

Extracted from ripe olives. It is best to only use Cold Pressed Virgin Olive Oil. Olive Oil is somewhat thicker than most other Vegetable Oils. Olive Oil is a fatty Oil with a long tradition of use in Skin and Hair Care. A good Oil for infusing/macerating herbs and flowers in. Very softening and protecting. Good to use for dry skin, preferably together with dry Oils such as Thistle or Sunflower Oil for use on the legs and feet. Use in Ointments and Massage Oils intended to increase circulation.

Rosehip Oil (extracted from the seeds of Rosa canina)

If a flower is left on a rose bush, the petals will fall off after it finishes blooming, and a small red fruit will form: that is the Rosehip. Rosehips have been used for centuries by the Incas as a source of nutrition (it is very high in Vitamin C), as well as an effective treatment for many skin problems. Pure Rosehip Oil has a high composition of Essential Fatty Acids: Linoleic and Linolenic, which help maintain healthy skin. As far as we know, Rosehip is one of the best vegetable source of Omega 3 Essential Fatty Acids and also a good source of Omega 6 Essential Fatty Acids. Rosehip Oil also contains natural tretinoin, a derivative of Retinol (Vitamin A), which replenishes and helps rebuild skin tissue. Rosehip Oil helps to reduce pigmentation and raised scar tissue, even on non-recent scars, and can be used to treat skin damaged, marked or scarred by: surgery, minor burns, stretch marks, acne, and sun exposure. Good for oily skin, sensitive skin, skin problems, and skin with large pores.

Sesame Oil (extracted from the seeds of Sesamum indicum)

A very fine culinary oil, especially for stir-fried foods, but it is important to note that this is not the toasted sesame oil generally sold for cooking, which should not be used on the skin. Sesame Oil also has good Skin Care properties and has a long tradition of being used as a Sun Oil, with a Sun Protection Factor of 2-3. It is good for Skin Care, as Hair Oil, and as a Baby or Massage Oil. It is a semi-fatty Oil. Nearly everyone tolerates this Oil very well and it can even be used around the eyes.

Shea Butter (extracted from the 3-5cm kernel of Butyrospermum parkii

In Skin Care products it has good anti-inflammatory properties and is useful for treating stretch marks, smaller wounds, dry skin and skin infections such as eczema. It has excellent softening properties, making the skin soft and supple. It also gives consistency to Ointments, Massage Bars, Creams, Massage Oils, Lip Balms and Body Butters. It protects the skin against dehydration and has a Sun Protection Factor of 2-3. Contains Phytosterols, which stimulates the formation and growth of new cells. Shea Butter works well in combination with Thistle Oil.

Shea Butter Oil (extracted from the 3-5cm kernel of Butyrospermum parkii)

Shea Butter Oil is produced by reducing the amount of stearic acid in the Shea Butter. For properties, see Shea Butter above.

Sunflower Oil (extracted from the seeds of Helianthus annuus)

Like Thistle Oil, Sunflower Oil contains a high level of Linoleic Acid, an Omega 6 Essential Fatty Acid, so it can be used in all kinds of products. It spreads easily and is absorbed relatively quickly by the skin. It can be used for all skin types, but because it is a dry Oil, it is best suited to oily skin. It also has excellent pore-reduction qualities, so good to use on skin with large pores. It is used in the same way as Thistle Oil.

Sweet Almond Oil (extracted from the kernel of Prunus amygdalus)

A classic, mild, semi-fatty Oil, which spreads nicely, makes the skin soft, smooth and supple. It is good for most skin types and can be used in Skin, Face and Massage Oils. Be sure not to buy the Bitter Almond Oil, which is not suitable for use on the skin. That particular Oil is never used in Skin Care, Massage or Aromatherapy as it may cause prussic acid poisoning. Aromantic do not stock Bitter Almond Oil.

Thistle Oil (Safflower Oil) (extracted from the seeds of Carthamus tinctorius)

A very useful Oil for the skin and face and as a Beauty Oil. Good for oily skin. It is thin and runny, belongs to the family of dry Oils and is easily absorbed by the skin. Thistle Oil contains up to 81% Linoleic Acid, an Omega 6 Essential Fatty Acid which plays a vital part in the body and skin's ability to maintain health. Linoleic Acid deficiency will result in different skin problems. Thistle Oil is good to include in most blends of Oil in different proportions to render them less fatty and therefore more easily absorbed by the skin.

Natural Moisturisers & Preservatives

Moisturisers

The skin needs more than just Fats and Oils. It is also important for the skin to maintain a certain level of moisture in its outermost layer. Moisture applied from the outside will only affect the outermost layer of the skin. In order to moisturise skin cells on the living inner layers it is necessary to approach these from within i.e. to drink lots of water, to ensure healthy, functioning skin. There are a vast number of substances, which are capable of binding water in the outermost layer of the skin, including these that Aromantic recommend and stock:

Botanical Glycerol Extracts

These are exciting Herbal Moisturising Extracts in Vegetable-based Glycerine. 70% vegetable Glycerine together with 30% water is used to extract the plant material. This method extracts most of the water and fat-soluble ingredients from the plants. This is therefore a combination product, which has a moisturising effect on the skin as well as the benefit of the herbal properties.

As Glycerine is water soluble it is very convenient to use in water-based products. Use in Shampoos, Liquid Soaps, Deodorants, Creams, Lotions, Gels, Face Masks, Hair Packs and Toothpastes.

Add the Extract when your recipe ingredients are less than 40°C or add it directly to cold products. Use at a dosage of 3-6% (3% contains 2% Glycerine and 6% contains 4% Glycerine). At the time of printing this Guide, Aromantic stock two Botanical Glycerol Extracts, namely Comfrey and Witch Hazel.

Carbamide INCI name: Urea

Urea, also known as Carbamide, is an organic compound of carbon, nitrogen, oxygen and hydrogen. It occurs in human urine in an average concentration of 2.4%, and in sweat in a concentration of 0.5-1%. For use in the cosmetic industry, it is synthetically produced using Ammonia and Carbon Dioxide. Pure Carbamide forms into colourless, odourless crystals, which have a cold, bitter, and salty taste. These crystals are easily dissolved in water and alcohol. Carbamide is used at a strength of 3-5% as a moisture-retaining and antiseptic agent in Deodorants and Foot and Hand Creams. It can be used at a strength of 10% in Creams for softening the feet. It has no known toxicity.

D-Panthenol INCI name: Panthenol

Pantothenic Acid (Vitamin B_5) is destroyed at temperatures over 50-60°C. D-Panthenol binds moisture in surface layers of the skin, is also active in the deeper layers as well as in the surface layers of nails and in the roots and strands of hair. It creates a protective film on hair and makes it soft and supple. D-Panthenol is used in Creams and Hair Products (particularly for dry, thin hair and sensitive scalp) in a concentration of 2-5%.

Research carried out on D-Panthenol shows that it: speeds up cell regeneration, which means that e.g. burns, acne and sores heal more quickly; soothes itchiness and infections; is antibacterial; increases skin pigmentation during sunbathing; and reduces the damaging effects of exposure to the sun.

Comfrey Glycerol Extract INCI name: Glycerine, Symphytum officinalis

From Organic Comfrey Root extracts. Contains mucilage, tannins and allantoin. Has soothing, moisturising, antiseptic and other well known healing properties. Good to use in Compresses, Shaving Creams, Shaving Water, Shampoos, Foam Baths and Toners. Has a faint herbal smell and has a beige/yellow colour. Dosage: 3-6%.

Glycerine INCI: Glycerine

Glycerine is a cheap, simple Moisturiser, which is used in a concentration of 3-5%. Both animal and vegetable-based Glycerines are available. (Aromantic only stock vegetable-based, guaranteed Kosher Glycerine.)

Honey Moisturiser INCI Name Hydroxy Propyltrimonium honey

Honey has been used in cosmetics since the beginning of time for its ability to moisturise the skin and hair. However, natural honey, a 75% active solution of disaccharides, is sticky in consistency and its moisturising properties are poor compared to other more commonly used materials such as Glycerine. Honey Moisturiser is a quaternised Honey; i.e. Honey converted to having its atoms bonded to four carbon atoms giving a low viscosity, 50% solid, clear, almost colourless liquid which has a pleasant feel on the skin and hair.

It has excellent moisture-binding properties, having twice the moisturising ability of Glycerine, a well-known and much used ingredient. Efficacy testing has shown that it has the ability to moisturise the hair, penetrate the endocuticle region and help to repair split ends.

Hyaluronic Acid INCI name: Aqua, Sodium Hyaluronate

Hyaluronic acid is what gives the skin its volume and fullness. Aging can result in the loss of hyaluronic acid, which in turn results in skin that has less volume and the formation of wrinkles and folds. Its hydrating properties result in increased skin smoothness, softening and decreased wrinkles. Its rejuvenating properties result in increased skin smoothness and softness. It is a common ingredient in skin care products. The product is a colourless gel. Dosage 1-5% in Hand and Body Lotions and Creams, Night Creams, Cleansers, Gels, Eye Gels and Serums, Foundations, Colour Cosmetics, Shaving Creams, Sun Care and Hair Care products. Add the Hyaluronic Acid during the third stage of making creams and lotions or when the temperature of the product you are making is between 40 and 35°C. Aromantic's Hyaluronic Acid is made by producing enzymes from a bacteria-based biofermentation process and NOT sourced from poultry (roosters' combs), as are many others.

Lactic Acid E270 INCI name: Lactic Acid (vegan)

Could be used as a Moisturiser but it is mostly used to regulate the pH in products. Use between 1-3 %. (Aromantic only stocks a non dairy Lactic Acid suitable for vegans.)

NFF Moisturiser INCI name: Sodium Lactate and Sodium PCA and Urea and Hydrolysed Vegetable Protein and Sodium pH

A Natural Moisturiser Factor, NFF Moisturiser is a pure, vegetable-based alternative to animal-based collagen or elastin. It is called NFF as an abbreviation of the Swedish term meaning "Natural Moisturising Factor" but trust me when I tell you that NFF is much easier to say! It consists of Sodium Lactate, Sodium PCA, Carbamide, Sodium Phosphate, extracts from asparagus and vegetable-based Soy Bean Protein, and a number of different substances, some of which occur naturally in the skin and help to bind moisture in the skin at deeper levels than Glycerine. NFF has been double-blind tested on people and results show that Creams containing NFF achieve a 60-70% better rate of moisture retention in the skin than Creams without it. NFF is used in Creams and Lotions in a concentration of 2-5%, depending on how much of a moisturising effect is required. Add NFF when temperature is less than 40°C (Third Stage).

Sorbitol (E 420) INCI name: Sorbitol

Like alcohol, Sorbitol occurs naturally in many types of fruit and berries. It is chemically synthesised from starch and glucose. Sorbitol can be used as a moisture retainer instead of Glycerine and gives a velvety feel to the skin. It is used at a strength of 2-5% in all sorts of Skin and Body Care products such as Creams, Liniments, Mouth Washes, Toothpastes, Hair Sprays, Face Masks and Deodorants, etc.

Witch Hazel Glycerol Extract INCI name: Glycerine, Hamamelis virginiana

Extracted from the leaves of organic Witch Hazel, which contains tannins and saponins. Works as an astringent and antiseptic. Use in Toners, Creams, Gels and Deodorants. Has the faint smell of Witch Hazel. Dosage: 3-6%.

Moisturisers - Safety Information

Moisturisers should not be used in large quantities. Glycerine and D-Panthenol should not be used in concentrations of more than 8-10%. Beyond this level they can cause itchy, syrupy feelings on the skin. Carbamide in large quantities will dissolve the outermost layer of skin consisting of dead skin cells.

Preservatives

Clean water and good hygiene are unfortunately not enough if a product is to keep for more than a few weeks. In this respect, Creams are as susceptible to bacteria as food is. So it is necessary to use some sort of Preservative. It is important to choose a Preservative, which will cover as wide a range as possible of the different sorts of bacteria, fungi and moulds which might apply.

Preservative 12 INCI: Phenoxyethanol, Ethylhexylglycerin.

This Preservative was introduced to the general cosmetics marketplace in early 2007 and was the most natural Preservative available to us at the time of printing this Guide. Aromantic have had it challenge-tested and we have found it works very well for people with sensitive skin. People who have previously reacted to the Potassium Sorbate in Preservative K seem to tolerate this new Preservative. Another advantage of this Preservative over Preservative K is that you don't need to think about the pH reduction and can use it up to a pH of 12. The only limitation is that it doesn't work in products that contain Detergents, such as Shampoos, Liquid Soaps, Shower Gels, and Foam Baths, etc.

As in Preservative K, Preservative 12 also contains phenoxyethanol but the producers have broken new ground here. An innovative multi-functional additive enhances the efficacy of phenoxyethanol. The addition of ethylhexylglycerin affects the interfacial tension at the cell membrane of microorganisms, improving the preservative activity of phenoxyethanol. Preservative 12 reduces the contact angle of water significantly. The wetting of surfaces is improved. With ethylhexylglycerin the contact of phenoxyethanol with the cell membrane of microorganisms can also be optimised. The antimicrobial efficacy of phenoxyethanol is therefore improved.

About using Preservative 12:

• Stable in varying temperatures – disperse into products at low and high temperatures.

• Stable in varying pH values – you can use it in products with a pH value up to 12.

• The product doesn't need to be reduced to a pH of 4.5 (as with Preservative K), therefore no Lactic Acid is needed.

• Can also tolerate a high salt content.

• Can be dissolved in water, Creams, Gels, Hydrolates, etc. and is broad spectrum, equally effective against bacteria, yeasts, mould and fungi.

• Doesn't impart any smell to the product.

• Ideal for preservation of clear, transparent Gels based on Carbomer (not used by Aromantic) or cellulose powder. Parabens give Gels a cloudiness, while using Preservative 12 keeps the Gels clear and transparent.

• Can be used on all kinds of Skin and Hair Care products, except for products containing Detergents so never use in Shampoos, 2-in-1 Shampoo & Conditioners, Shower Gels, Liquid Soaps, and Foam Baths where a high percentage of Detergents results in loss of efficacy of Preservative 12.

• Especially recommended for products that treat sensitive skin.

• The easiest is to add it to the Third Stage in products. Use from 0.5% to 1%. As this is a new Preservative for you I recommend using 0.6%. For example, for 100ml/g, use 0.6ml/g or for 1000ml/g, use 6ml/g. When using Herbal Infusions in your Recipes, I would recommend adding 1% of Preservative 12.

• You can just replace Parabens and Preservative K with Preservative 12 in your old Recipes except in Recipes that call for the use of Detergents, as previously discussed.

Preservative K INCI name: Benzyl Alcohol, Phenoxyethanol, and Potassium Sorbate

A relatively natural Preservative used by green cosmetics companies worldwide, it is a liquid Preservative based on Potassium Sorbate and Alcohols. The fungicidal and fungistatic properties of Sorbic Acid (found in the totally natural Potassium Sorbate) form the basis of the effectiveness of Preservative K. Potassium Sorbate is also added for the its qualities of stability and solubility. The spectrum of activity is supplemented and balanced by the use of Benzyl Alcohol (effective against Gram-positive bacteria) and Phenoxyethanol (effective against Gram-negative bacteria).

Preservative K offers a broad, balanced spectrum of effect against bacteria, yeasts and mould fungi. It will only work in cosmetic products with a skin-friendly pH value up to 5.5. The typical dosage of preservative K is 0.5-1.5%.

As a result of the Potassium Sorbate in the formulation, Preservative K raises the pH of the product. After it has been incorporated into the cosmetic product, the pH value of the product therefore has to be adjusted. After having added all of your Raw Materials, Essential Oils and Preservative K, then test the pH. If over 5.5, add from 0.3-0.5% Lactic Acid and retest the pH. When under 5.5pH, your products will keep for 1.5-3 years, depending on the product. When testing a Cream, smear the Litmus Paper with the Cream and scrape it off after 1 minute to reveal the pH. If you have a liquid product e.g. Shampoos, simply dip the litmus paper in for 30 seconds and the colour will be easily revealed.

Despite the fact that it contains synthetic chemicals, Preservative K is now accepted by the Soil Association as part of an organic cosmetic product that can be labelled 'made with organic ingredients'.

Parabens INCI name of Aromantic's blend: Phenoxethanol (and) Methylparaben (and) Ethylparaben (and) Propylparaben

Different types of Parabens, often a mixture of a few, are probably the most frequently used Preservatives and are tolerated by most people. Aromantic's blend of Parabens is used by the food industry and it does not contain the controversial Butylparaben. Parabens have a liquid consistency, which makes them easy to use. Use in a concentration of 0.4-0.8%, depending on the raw materials you are using. As a rule, the more Herbal Infusions used in a product, the more Preservative one will need to use.

If one is allergic to Preservatives, or would rather not use them for other reasons, then it is necessary to make small quantities of products and keep them refrigerated. One can also experiment with Essential Oils as Preservatives, such as Tea Tree, in which case the Oils will need to be used in a concentration of at least 3% (90 drops to 100ml). **Note:** this dosage may make the Cream very strong, which may irritate the skin. Also it will give the Cream a very strong odour of the Essential Oil that you used.

Making Creams

Making your own Creams & Moisturisers is simple, easy and interesting. There are a few simple rules, which must be followed but beyond these there are endless possibilities for inventing and making your own unique Creams for different purposes – and you'll know exactly what the Creams contain. If there is an ingredient you or your client is allergic to, you can often leave it out or replace it with something else.

A Cream is an emulsion of oil and water. One liquid is held suspended in another and it makes it easier to think of mayonnaise as a good example. In order to mix oil and water you will need an Emulsifier – a medium that enables normally non-mixable ingredients to mix together. Aromantic's MF and VE Emulsifiers are both used as ingredients in the Scandinavian food industry to make bread and vegan ice cream. This shows that they are both very safe Emulsifiers to use as they are edible. The VE Emulsifier added during the Fat Stage and the MF Emulsifier during the Water Stage.

NB: We never recommend using Paraffin-based Emulsifiers such as Emulsifying Wax or Pola Wax.

Table 2: Conversion Table for ingredients in Creams

Shea Butter	1g = 1.5ml
Cetyl Alcohol	1g = 3ml
MF Emulsifier	1g = 2.5ml
VE Emulsifier	1g = 2ml
Essential Oil	0.5 ml = 12-15 drops (approximately)

For metric-US Conversion Tables, see pages 99-101. For a more comprehensive product conversion table see pages 97 & 98. For a more comprehensive Essential Oil conversion table, see page 99.

Equipment required for making Creams

  2x Double boilers (bain-maries)

  Spatula

  Whisk

  Measuring jug

  Measuring spoons

  Thermometer (for up to 100°C)

You will also need weighing scales but if you don't have one, you can use the Conversion Table on the previous page to find an alternative way of measuring your ingredients. It is important to be particularly careful with hygiene when using water in products.

Recipes for Base Creams

NB All Recipes add up to 100ml/g.

Simple Moisturiser

- **Fat Stage (75-80°C)**
6ml Sweet Almond Oil

3ml Thistle Oil

2g Cetyl Alcohol

2.5g VE Emulsifier

- **Water Stage (75-80°C)**
4g MF Emulsifier

76ml Boiling Spring Water

2ml/g Glycerine

12 drops (0.6ml/g) Preservative

- **Third Stage (40-35°C)**
2ml NFF Moisturiser

1ml/g Vitamin E Oil (undiluted)

- **Fourth Stage (30-25°C)**
20 drops Essential Oil

Calendula Cream

- **Fat Stage (75-80°C)**
6ml Vegetable Oil

2g Shea Butter

2g Cetyl Alcohol

3g VE Emulsifier

- **Water Stage (75-80°C)**
4.5g MF Emulsifier

75ml Boiling Spring Water

4ml/g Glycerine

12 drops (0.6ml/g) Preservative

- **Third stage 40-35°C)**
1ml Calendula CO_2 Extract

0.5ml Vitamin E Oil (undiluted)

- **Fourth Stage (30-25°C)**
20 drops Essential Oil

Note: use double the amount of Preservative when you use Herbal Infusions in place of Boiling Spring Water. This is because Herbal Infusions naturally contain a lot of bacteria and fungi.

Recipes for other types of Creams

These can be created by making adjustments to the Base Recipe.

Vitamin Cream for Dry/ Sensitive Skin

- **Fat Stage (75-80°C)**

8ml Apricot Kernel Oil

2g Shea Butter

2g Cetyl Alcohol

2.5g VE Emulsifier

1-3 drops Carotene

- **Water Stage (75-80°C)**

4g MF Emulsifier

68ml Boiling Spring Water

4ml/g Glycerine

12 drops (0.6ml/g) Preservative

- **Third Stage (40-35°C)**

5ml Borage Oil

2ml Vitamin E Oil (undiluted)

1ml/g Vitamin A Palmitate

- **Fourth Stage (30-25°C)**

20 drops Essential Oil

Highly effective Moisturiser

- **Fat Stage (75-80°C)**

8ml Jojoba Oil

2g Shea Butter

1g Cetyl Alcohol

2.5g VE Emulsifier

- **Water Stage (75-80°C)**

4.5g MF Emulsifier

74ml Boiling Spring Water

12 drops (0.6ml/g) Preservative

- **Third Stage (40-35°C)**

4ml NFF Moisturiser

1ml/g Vitamin E Oil (undiluted)

- **Fourth Stage (30-25°C)**

20 drops Essential Oil

Cleanser Cream

- **Fat Stage (75-80°C)**

8ml Castor Oil

8ml Jojoba or Sweet Almond Oil

2g Cetyl Alcohol

1g Cocoa Butter

3g VE Emulsifier

- **Water Stage (75-80°C)**

5g MF Emulsifier

62ml Boiling Spring Water

5ml/g Sorbitol/Glycerine

12 drops (0.6ml/g) Preservative

- **Third Stage (40-35°C)**

4ml Beta Detergent

1ml/g Vitamin E (undiluted)

- **Fourth Stage (30-25°C)**

20 drops Essential Oil

Dry Skin Cream

- **Fat Stage (75-80°C)**
2g Cocoa Butter

3ml Olive Oil

7ml Sweet Almond Oil

3ml Thistle Oil

2g Cetyl Alcohol

2.5g VE Emulsifier

- **Water Stage (75-80°C)**
4.5g MF Emulsifier

70ml Boiling Spring Water

2ml/g Glycerine

12 drops (0.6ml/g) Preservative

- **Third Stage (40-35°C)**
0.5ml/g Vitamin E Oil (undiluted)

2ml/g NFF Moisturiser

- **Fourth Stage (30-25°C)**
20 drops Essential Oil

Basic Method for making all Creams

1) **Fat Stage:** Heat the Fat Stage ingredients in a double boiler until all of the ingredients have melted and the temperature has risen to 75-80°C. There is no need to use a whisk at this stage.

2) **Water Stage:** After boiling the Spring Water in a Kettle, measure it according to the Recipe and pour it over the MF Emulsifier and the Glycerine, Sorbitol and Preservative, which you have put into a separate double boiler.

3) Whisk the Water Stage ingredients well together, making sure that the MF Emulsifier powder is fully dissolved in the water and that you don't have any lumps. Then allow the mixture to heat to 75-80°C.

4) When both Fat and Water Stages are over 75°C, remove both double boilers from the hob, keeping the Water Stage mixture hot by leaving it on the top half of the double boiler.

5) Now pour the melted Fat Stage into the Water Stage in a thin, steady stream, while continuously whisking the mixture from side to side for 5 minutes. If necessary, use a spatula to scrape the mixture from the sides of the saucepan (or bowl).

6) Allow the mixture to cool, stirring all the time. You can speed up by the cooling process by replacing the hot water in the double boiler with very COLD water. In the process of cooling down, the mixture becomes a Cream and will reach its thickest consistency when it is has cooled down to room temperature.

7) **Third Stage:** Stir in the Third Stage ingredients when the mixture has cooled to under 40°C.

8) **Fourth Stage:** Continue stirring until the mixture has cooled to under 30°C, then thoroughly mix in the Essential Oils.

9) Pour the Cream into one big jar or smaller jars and label.

Tips for making Creams successfully

- If you wish to make the Dry Skin Care Cream fluffier, add 20-30ml Aloe Vera Gel to this amount of Cream and reduce the Boiling Spring Water accordingly (see Recipe for Gels on page 37).

- Use double the amount of Preservative when you use Herbal Infusions in place of Boiling Spring Water. This is because Herbal Infusions naturally contain a lot of bacteria and fungi.

• To ensure a smooth Cream, use an electric stick blender to blend the ingredients for 1 minute after adding the Fat Stage to the Water Stage, then continue whisking, as directed in the Method, for 4 more minutes.

• To ensure a smooth Cream, use an electric stick blender to blend the ingredients for 1 minute after adding the Fat Stage to the Water Stage, then continue whisking, as directed in the Method, for 4 more minutes.

• When whisking or stirring, it is important to touch the bottom of the saucepan, or bowl, so as not to introduce air into the mixture.

• As you are making a whole litre of Cream, you don't need to add the Essential Oils to the whole amount straight away; you can add Essential Oils when putting the Cream into smaller jars.

• Shelf life of these Creams is 1.5-2 years.

• For more Recipes, see our section on Cosmetic Information, 'Making your own Creams' on Aromantic's website.

• Practising Aromatherapists can combine the Creams with Essential Oils and other ingredients suited to the special needs of their clients.

Adapting Cream Recipes and Method to make Lotions

If you have made a bigger amount of a Cream Recipe and you would now like to make a Lotion, you can take 100ml of the Cream and add 100ml cold Spring Water, little by little, whisking all the while.

As the last step, add 1 drop of Preservative for each 10ml of water you added. For example, if you added 500ml extra water, you would need to add 50 drops of Preservative, which is equivalent to 2ml or 2g, if you prefer measuring it or weighing it this way.

Adding value to your Creams and Lotions by adding other raw materials

Essential Oil Blends for Creams

Examples of Essential Oil Blends which can be used to enhance 100ml of your Cream (25 drops=approximately 1ml/g):

Blend 1 - Good All Rounder

15 drops Lavender

5 drops Geranium

Blend 2 - Young Skin

15 drops Orange

5 drops Ylang Ylang

Blend 3 - Mature or Men's Skin

6 drops Rosewood

7 drops Sandalwood

Blend 4 - All Skin Types 1

15 drops Rosewood

5 drops Orange

Blend 5 - All Skin Types 2

10 drops Sandalwood

3 drops Orange

Blend 6 - Oily Skin

15 drops Orange

5 drops Geranium

Examples of Essential Oil Blends that can be used to enhance 1000ml/1 litre of your Cream:

Blend for Dry Skin (Orange)

60 drops Orange

40 drops Geranium

40 drops Lavender

10 drops Benzoin

Blend for Dry Skin (Mandarin)

90 drops Mandarin

30 drops Sandalwood

15 drops Neroli (undiluted)

8 drops Jasmine (undiluted)

Cream Recipe variations - Vegetable Oils

Using the DRY SKIN CREAM Recipe on page 26 as a basis, see Table 3 below to make different Creams for different types and conditions.

Table 3: Dry Skin Cream Recipe Variations

To change it to a Sensitive Skin Cream	
Replace	**with**
3ml Olive Oil &	8ml Apricot or Peach Kernel Oil
7ml Sweet Almond Oil	2ml Macadamia Nut Oil
To change it to a Luxury Cream for Sensitive Skin	
Replace	**with**
3ml Olive Oil &	6ml Apricot or Peach Kernel Oil,
7ml Sweet Almond Oil	1ml Macadamia Nut Oil & 5ml Rosehip Oil, (Add the Rosehip in the Third Stage).
	NB Reduce the water content by 2ml
To change it to a Cream for Mature Skin	
Replace	**with**
3ml Olive Oil &	6ml Macadamia Nut Oil
7ml Sweet Almond Oil	4ml Apricot or Peach Kernel Oil
Cream for Oily or Large-pored Skin (NB Use the SIMPLE MOISTURISER Recipe on page 24 as a basis)	
Replace	**with**
6ml Sweet Almond Oil	5ml Rosehip Oil (but add it in the Third Stage)

Our most frequently asked questions about making Creams and Lotions

Q) Is it necessary to add Preservatives to Aromantic Creams and Lotions?

A) Yes, you must always add Preservatives when there is water in the product. We recommend between 0.5%-0.6% Preservative. If you use Herbal Infusions in the products you must add 0.8%-1.0% Preservative. Herbs contain a lot of bacteria, which is why you need to add extra. It can be dangerous not to add Preservatives to water-based products, as the bacteria are invisible when they grow. Fungi, on the other hand, are obvious by their green/blue colour at the top of the Cream. Without Preservatives, the products will keep in a cold fridge for up to 2 weeks. Just treat them like dairy products and you won't go wrong.

For 100ml of finished product use: 10 drops (0.5ml/g) Parabens; OR 12 drops (0.6ml/g) Preservative 12; OR 20 drops (1ml/g) Preservative K along with 10 drops (0.5ml/g) Lactic Acid. Preservative 12 will not work with Detergents and if using Preservative K, the pH in products must be below 5.5.

Q) Can I use Grape Seed Extract as a Preservative?

A) No. This has been tried by the food industry and it has been found that the protection it gives is not broad enough to prevent many bacteria forming. Our clients who have tried it usually find fungi growths on top of their Creams within 3 months.

Q) My Cream became too runny!

A) With a VE/MF Cream, this is usually caused by too little MF added to the water and other ingredients. Often it is not mixed thoroughly and the MF powder is left at the bottom or around the edges. Using an electric stick blender can prevent this and help the Cream thicken by itself. It is also very important that both the Water and Fat Stages are over 75°C and that the Fat Stage is poured little by little into the Water Stage. Both Stages need to be kept in hot water when stirred together for 5 minutes. One tip is to sprinkle some Xanthan Gum (maximum 0.5%) on to the top of the Cream as you blend it with an stick blender. Bear in mind that Creams will also thicken naturally until they have reached normal room temperature (20°C in Northern Europe).

Q) My cream is too thick!

A) After your cream is made, you can whisk in more cold water, little by little, until you achieve the consistency you want. If you want to make a lighter cream you can try blending it with an electric mixer but be careful not to introduce air bubbles to your cream. You could also add some aloe vera gel to your cream, which makes it fluffy and has a very nice feeling on the skin.

Q) My Cream is too grainy and lumpy.

A) This is most likely caused by not mixing in the MF powder thoroughly. Blend with an electric stick blender for 5 minutes to create a smooth consistency or if that doesn't work, heat the Cream up to 75°C and repeat the process in the Method again.

Q) The Cream or Lotion I make becomes greyish.

A) This sometimes happens when you use Herbal Infusions or Decoctions in your Cream or Lotion. Add 2 drops of Carotene during the Fat Stage to mask this effect. Be aware that the yellow colour of the Carotene will fade if exposed to direct sunlight. If you want your Cream to be white, try adding the whitener, Titanium Dioxide. Mix it into a little Glycerine and then add it to the Cream at the end.

Q) The Cream has an unpleasant smell.

A) Several things can cause this. Firstly, you may have used a smelly Vegetable Oil such as Borage, which naturally has a 'mouldy' smell. Organic Rosehip has a stronger smell than the non-Organic Oil. You may have used Vegetable Oil such as Wheatgerm Oil, which has gone rancid. Vitamin A Oil also has an unpleasant smell. Most raw materials have a smell, some more than others. One way is to use Vegetable Oils such as Evening Primrose instead of Borage Oil and use Vitamin E Oil (undiluted) instead of Wheatgerm Oil. You could also use deodorised Thistle Oil instead of the Organic one. You could also try to mask the smell by adding base note Essential Oils such as Benzoin, Sandalwood, Cedarwood or Patchouli.

Q) The Cream is too heavy. How can I make it lighter?

A) You could add a little more water to the Cream if it is not too runny. Using a stick blender to mix your Cream will make it lighter. Next time you make it you could also reduce the amount of water at the Water Stage by 10-25% and then replace it with 10-25% light Aloe

Vera Gel after the Third Stage. The Gel needs to be thin so that you can pour it into a bottle. If it is too thick it will create a Cream with the consistency of chewing gum. Gel will make the Cream lighter and fluffier. You can also make a Vegetal Cream. This is slightly trickier to make but Vegetal Creams are much lighter. See *Recipe No 18 Vegetal in Creams and Lotions* (not included in this Guide). Be sure that the amount of Preservative is correct for the finished volume of Cream.

Q) What kind of water should I use in my products?

A) I like to use a well-known brand of bottled Still Spring Water in my Creams. In the cosmetic industry they use distilled water but to me that is a lifeless product.

Q) Can I use an electric stick blender to make my Cream?

A) Yes. Use it to mix the Fat Stage and Water Stage together for 5 minutes. You can also use it when the Cream cools down. The result will be a smoother Cream with a lighter, finer texture. Commercial companies use large electric blenders to make their products. **Note:** Our Starter Pack No 1 'How to make your own Skin Care Creams' contains pre-measured quantities of ingredients so ingredients so that you do not need to use scales.

Making Cleansers, Exfoliates, Peelers & Toners

Cleansers

Cleansing the skin is the essential first step in the basic 3-step beauty routine of Cleansing, Toning, and Moisturising. Cleansing with a good quality Cleanser twice a day – once in the morning and once before going to bed at night – assures the removal of surface impurities, traces of make-up, and excessive oiliness and enhances the skin's ability to breathe. Cleansing is necessary for all skin types.

Raw materials that are used in Skin Cleansers

Vegetable Oils absorb fat-soluble dirt. The fattier Oils such as Castor Oil or Macadamia Nut Oil are not absorbed as quickly by the skin and are therefore ideal for this purpose. Vegetable Oils can be used on their own (as Cleansing Oils), or as part of a Cleansing Cream, Lotion, or Gel. Vegetable Oils also restore Oil to the skin and can be used where Surface Cleansing Agents (Detergents) are included in your product as Detergents remove fats and oils from your skin.

Surface Cleansing Agents (Detergents) have, as the description suggests, a cleansing effect and, in the appropriate quantity, are an excellent ingredient to include in Cleansing products. They can be mixed into Cleansing Creams, Lotions, or Gels. Be cautious with the use of Detergents for people with sensitive skin as these agents can irritate the skin.

Recipes for Cleansing Lotions

This type of Recipe is based on using high quantities of Vegetable Oils as Cleansing remedies. In order to use these quantities of Vegetable Oils, we need to use a special Emulsifier called Emulsifan CB. Emulsifan CB is used when we need to add a lot of Oils to our products. Emulsifan CB is a water-to-fat Emulsifier. (VE & MF are fat-to-water Emulsifiers).

Cleansing Lotion

A good natural Lotion for non-sensitive skin (if using a mild Detergent), which can be easily removed with water.

- **Fat Stage (75-80°C)**

2g Beeswax

6g Emulsifan CB

26g/ml Sweet Almond Oil

10g Castor Oil

- **Water Stage (75-80°C)**

3ml/g Sorbitol or Glycerine

49ml Boiling Spring Water

contd over/

- **Third Stage (40-35°C)**

12 drops (0.6ml/g) Preservative

3g Beta Detergent

- **Fourth Stage (30-25°C)**

15-20 drops Essential Oils of your choice

Method for making Cleansing Lotions

1) Heat the Fat Stage in a double boiler until all the ingredients have melted and the temperature has risen to 75-80°C.

2) Heat the Water Stage in a saucepan to the same temperature.

3) Add the Water Stage to the Fat Stage, pouring slowly in a thin, steady stream while whisking the mixture all the time.

4) Keep the Lotion mixture warm (keep water in the bottom pan of double boiler hot) and whisk the mixture from side to side in the bottom of the saucepan for a further 5 minutes, using a spatula to scrape the mixture from the sides of the pan.

5) Allow the Lotion to cool (you can speed this up by immersing the pan into a large pan of COLD water), stirring all the time. It is important to touch the bottom of the pan as you stir so as not to introduce air into the Cream.

6) Starting at 40°C, add the Third Stage ingredients.

7) Continue stirring until the mixture has cooled to 30°C, and then mix in the Essential Oils thoroughly.

8) Pour into bottles and label.

Exfoliating, Scrubbing and Peeling Agents

Exfoliating, Scrubbing & Peeling Agents are completely natural ingredients for gentle or more thorough exfoliating or peeling, which you can add to your homemade or shop-bought products such as Creams, Gels, and Shower Gels, etc. Add the Agent by stirring it evenly into your product with a clean, dry teaspoon, adding a little at a time until you are happy with the texture. Exfoliating or peeling is normally done before toning and then moisturising the skin.

These are the Exfoliating/Scrubbing Agents that we stock:

Dead Sea Salt (Fine)/Sea Salt (Fine)

An Exfoliating Agent to remove dead skin cells, help to draw out toxins & to stimulate growth of new skin. Use from 2 tablespoons in Baths. For Healing Baths use 500g-1kg per bath. The granules are fine and round and don't tear and damage the skin.

Exfoliant 'Cupuaçu'

These fine bio-scrub particles with a faint smell of chocolate provide a stimulating, yet gentle scrub action with low abrasion on the skin and is therefore gentle enough to use on the face. Add 1-10% in your products, according to the desired feel on your skin. It can be applied to face and body daily.

From the seeds of the Cupuaçu tree, harvested in a sustainable development managed within the South American rainforest. Approved by Eco-Cert as an Organic product. The manufacturer works with nature, obtaining its precious resources with care and responsibility.

Cupuaçu fruits are oblong, brown, and fuzzy, 20cm (8in) long, 1-2 kg (2-4lb) in weight, and covered with a thick (4-7mm) hard exocarp. Several aspects of Cupuaçu make it interesting. The flowers, for example, are the biggest of the genre. They do not grow on the log, as the Theobromine, but in the branches. Their seeds are industrialised for the production of a Wax Butter with excellent quality, from which an Oil is refined and filtered and which has fantastic properties for the cosmetic industry. Exfoliant 'Cupuaçu' has a faint smell of chocolate as the tree is related to Cacao.

Properties

The seeds contain phytosterols, which act at a cellular level by regulating the lipids on the superficial layer of the skin. Phytosterols are also used for skin and ulcer treatment by local application, order to stimulate the scarring process. The structure of the phytosterols is formed by beta-sitosterol, stigmasterol, and campesterol. The beta-sitosterol properties are similar to the chemical structure of cholesterol. It represents more than 70% of the unsaponifiable fraction of the Cupuaçu Butter.

Benefits

Improves circulation

Removes dead skin cells

Rejuvenates the skin

Physically stimulates skin through massage

Removes dirt from pores

Leaves a soft feeling to the skin

Revitalisation properties

For use in Skin and Body Care

Shower Gels

Liquid and Solid Soaps

Cleansers

Peelers

Massage Oils

and Hand and Feet preparations.

Apricot Kernel Powder

Use in a concentration of 1-5%. To add thorough exfoliating and scrubbing properties to Creams & Soaps. It is best used for body parts that need and tolerate vigorous peeling such as the hands, the feet, legs and bottom. **NB** Do not use on the face!

Chondrus Crispus Flakes

For gentle exfoliating and Skin Protection. The Flakes will help to activate blood microcirculation, eliminate toxins and improve the process of weight reduction. Use 1-6% in Solid Soaps, Liquid Soaps, Shower Gels and Gels.

Jojoba Exfoliating Grains

Are extracted from the waxes of the Jojoba plant. The grains are smooth and do not irritate the skin. The fine grain size is excellent for exfoliating dead skin and improving circulation. Use between 2-10% in Shower Gels, Oils, Gels and Creams. Don't heat over 60°C. Never whisk the product that you've added Jojoba Exfoliating grains to; stir into the product at the end of the Recipe instead. You can also add the Grains after you've made your products – just make sure you stir them in evenly without breaking up the Grains.

These are the Peeling Agents we stock:

AHA Natural Fruit Extract

A natural Peeling Agent that has 12-17% Glycolic Acid. AHA Natural Fruit Extract is a concentrated blend of five botanical extracts: bilberry, sugar cane, sugar maple, orange, and lemon, making it a natural source of several AHAs (Alpha Hydroxy Acids). Alpha Hydroxy Acids have been shown to promote smoother, younger looking skin by increasing the rate of cell renewal and have excellent moisturising properties. Maximum efficacy with minimum irritation. AHA Natural Fruit Extract is 55% active at a pH of 4. Dosage in products: 5-15% added to your recipes at the third stage, or under 40°C.

NB Never use around the eyes and do a skin sensitivity test on a patch of skin if you are a first-time user of any AHA product.

Lactic Acid

Often used for lowering the pH value of product to below 5.5 so that it can be used in combination with Preservative K. Lactic Acid can be used as a Peeling agent for its AHA effect. Use 3% in Creams and 1% in Lotions. It also has moisturising qualities.

Beta Detergent

A Detergent for Shampoos, Shower Gels & Liquid Soaps, Beta Detergent is produced from coconut oil, is often used a Secondary Detergent, and can be used as a mild Peeling ingredient in Peeling and Cleansing Creams, Lotions & Gels.

Sugar Detergent

A secondary 'help' Detergent made from sugar, Sugar Detergent can also be used as a mild Peeling ingredient in Peeling and Cleansing Creams, Lotions & Gels.

Recipes for Exfoliating Creams

An Exfoliating Cream is abrasive and removes dead skin cells. The Base in this case consists of a Cream made with Castor Oil with the addition of vegetable-based exfoliating granules such as Jojoba Exfoliating Grains. To use the Exfoliating Cream, wet the face first then apply the Exfoliating Cream. Massage it in well then wash off with water. These Recipes make 100ml.

Exfoliating Cream - All Skin Types

- **Fat Stage (75-80°C)**

8ml Thistle Oil

10ml Castor Oil

3g Shea Butter

2g Cetyl Alcohol

3g VE Emulsifier

- **Water Stage (75-80°C)**

5g MF Emulsifier

63ml Boiling water

3ml/g Sorbitol

12 drops (0.6ml/g) Preservative

- **Third Stage (40-35°C)**

1g Vitamin E Oil (undiluted) or Ground Loofah Flakes

- **Fourth Stage (30-25°C)**

10 drops Lemon Essential Oil

8 drops Geranium Essential Oil

- **Fifth Stage (30-25°C)**

3g Jojoba Exfoliating Grains

Exfoliating Cream - Dry/Mature skin

- **Fat Stage (75-80°C)**

10ml Castor Oil

6ml Macadamia Oil

2g Shea Butter

2g Cetyl Alcohol

3g VE Emulsifier

- **Water Stage (75-80°C)**

5g MF Emulsifier

67ml Rose Water

3ml/g Sorbitol or Glycerine

12 drops Preservative

- **Third Stage (40-35°C)**

2ml/g Vitamin E Oil (undiluted)

- **Fourth Stage (30-25°C)**

10 drops Geranium Essential Oil

5 drops Petitgrain Essential Oil

5 drops Lavender Essential Oil

- **Fifth Stage (30-25°C)**

2-5g Jojoba Exfoliating Grains

Method for making Cleansing and Exfoliating Creams

(Same Method as MF/VE Emulsifier Creams.)

1) **Fat Stage:** Heat the Fat Stage ingredients in a double boiler until all of the ingredients have melted and the temperature has risen to 75-80°C. There is no need to use a whisk at this stage.

2) **Water Stage:** After boiling the Spring Water in a Kettle, measure it according to the Recipe and pour it over the MF Emulsifier and the Glycerine, which you have put into a separate double boiler.

3) Whisk the Water Stage ingredients well together, making sure that the MF Emulsifier powder is fully dissolved in the water and that you don't have any lumps. Then allow the mixture to heat to 75-80°C.

4) When both Fat and Water Stages are over 75°C, remove both double boilers from the hob, keeping the Water Stage mixture hot by leaving it on the top half of the double boiler.

5) Now pour the melted Fat Stage into the Water Stage in a thin, steady stream, while continuously whisking the mixture from side to side for 5 minutes. If necessary, use a spatula to scrape the mixture from the sides of the saucepan (or bowl).

6) Allow the mixture to cool, stirring all the time. You can speed up by the cooling process by replacing the hot water in the double boiler with very COLD water. In the process of cooling down, the mixture becomes a Cream and will reach its thickest consistency when it is has cooled down to room temperature.

7) **Third Stage:** Stir in the Third Stage ingredients when the mixture has cooled to under 40°C.

8) **Fourth Stage:** Continue stirring until the mixture has cooled to under 30°C, then thoroughly mix in the Essential Oils.

9) **Fifth Stage:** Finally stir in the Jojoba Exfoliating Grains. Note: Don't stir the Grains too vigorously as they may disintegrate if you do so.

Skin Toners

Like Cleansers, Skin Toners are an essential part of the basic 3-step beauty routine of Cleansing, Toning, and

Moisturising. Skin Toners are applied after using a Cleanser and before applying a Moisturiser.

They act as astringents, cleaning and reducing the size of the pores and wrinkles so that dust and dirt will not enter as easily – avoiding further skin problems.

Toners can also be used to disinfect and freshen up the skin, leaving a trace of Essential Oil. They are easily applied with cotton wool or can be sprayed on and then wiped off with cotton wool.

Dry/Mature Skin Toner

80ml Rose Water

15ml Neroli Water

5ml Witch Hazel Glycerol Extract

Sensitive Skin Toner

60ml Neroli Water

20ml Rose Water

14ml Geranium Water

3ml Comfrey Glycerol Extract

3ml Aloe Vera Concentrate

General Method for making Skin Toners

1) Simply measure all raw materials in a measuring cylinder or beaker.

2) Pour into a 100ml bottle.

3) Secure the cap and label.

Tips for making Skin Toners

• The shelf life of these Skin Toners without added Preservatives is 1 year. If Preservatives are added, the shelf life is increased to 2 years. Simply add 10 extra drops of Preservative per 100ml.

• Use Hydrolates that suit your skin type or condition.

Making Gels

Gels are fun and easy to make and easy to apply to the skin. A Gel is made from water and a Thickening Agent. Other ingredients are added for various purposes, depending on what the Gel is used for. Gels are usually either clear or semi-opaque. A Gel is used in products where it is desirable to have little or no Fats or Oils and is best mixed using a water-based medium. If a small amount of Fat is required in the Gel, up to 5% Vegetable Oil can be added. Gels are also able to carry an Essential Oil content of up to a maximum of 5% but be aware that the Oil may make the Gel cloudy. Too much of either of these ingredients can result in an uneven distribution in the Gel. The thicker the Gel is, the more Vegetable or Essential Oil it will be able to carry.

Which Thickening Agents to use in the manufacture of Gels is a question of taste, or rather of 'feeling' i.e. how the Gel feels when applied to the skin and then how it feels when its moisture has evaporated. The Thickening Agents retain moisture, protect the skin and can also be astringent. The skin does not absorb them.

These Thickening Agents can either be wholly synthetic, such as a polymer, or wholly natural, such as a polysaccharide.

Natural polysaccharides are extracted from plants or algae and are found in large quantities in:

Carrageen (extracted from the seaweed Carrageen)

Alginates (extracted from different algae)

Pectin (extracted from citrus peel)

Cellulose Gum (extracted from wood fibre). Makes clear Gels.

Xanthan Gum (produced by Xanthomonas campestris bacteria through the fermentation of glucose - no bacteria are left in the finished product).

We prefer Xanthan Gum but any of the other Thickening Agents may be used. Xanthan Gum is used as a Thickening Agent in medical, food and cosmetic products.

Recipes for Gels

These Recipes make approximately 100ml.

Base Aloe Gel

- **Stage 1**
88ml Spring Water
1g/2ml/$^1/_2$ tsp Xanthan Gum

- **Stage 2**
10ml Aloe Vera Concentrate
12 drops (0.6ml/g) Preservative

Cellulite Gel

- **Stage 1**

97ml Spring Water

1g/2ml/$^1/_2$ tsp Xanthan Gum

- **Stage 2**

10 drops (0.5ml/g) Preservative

20 drops Rosemary Essential Oil

5 drops Sweet Fennel Essential Oil

5 drops Juniper Oil

Scrubbing Gel

- **Stage 1**

94ml Spring Water

1g/2ml/$^1/_2$ tsp Xanthan Gum

- **Stage 2**

10 drops (0.5ml/g) Preservative

3g Apricot Kernel Powder

7 drops Cypress Essential Oil

10 drops Grapefruit Essential Oil

7 drops Lavender Essential Oil

3 drops Spearmint Essential Oil

Strong Muscle Gel*

- **Stage 1**

92ml Spring Water

1g/2ml/$^1/_2$ tsp Xanthan Gum

- **Stage 2**

2ml NFF Moisturiser

5ml White Crystal Essential Oil/ Crystal blend (or an Essential Oil blend of Peppermint, Lavender and Camphor)

Tea Tree Gel*

- **Stage 1**

82.5ml Spring Water

1g/2ml/$^1/_2$ tsp Xanthan Gum

- **Stage 2**

6 drops (0.3ml/g) Preservative

10ml Aloe Vera Concentrate

2ml D-Panthenol Moisturiser

3ml Tea Tree Essential Oil

1ml Lavender Essential Oil

*NB: Before using the Strong Muscle and Tea Tree Gels

Because of the high quantities of Essential Oils in these products, be sure to do a skin allergy test. See page 2 for how to do the test. Once you're satisfied that your skin is not reacting adversely to it, you can apply the Strong Muscle or Tea Tree Gel on small patches of the skin such as in the crook of the arm, or (for the Tea Tree Gel) pimples and athlete's foot, etc.

After Sun Gel

- **Stage 1**

80ml Spring Water

1g/2ml/$^1/_2$ tsp Xanthan Gum

- **Stage 2**

12 drops (0.6ml/g) Preservative

10ml Aloe Vera Concentrate

2ml NFF Moisturiser

5ml St. John's Wort Oil

20 drops Lavender Essential Oil

10 drops Spearmint Essential Oil

Foot Gel

- **Stage 1**

90ml Spring Water

1g/2ml/$\frac{1}{2}$ tsp Xanthan Gum

- **Stage 2**

2g Carbamide crystals

2ml NFF Moisturiser

2ml Lactic Acid

35 drops Tea Tree Essential Oil

5 drops Sage Essential Oil

5 drops Lavender Essential Oil

6 drops (0.3ml/g) Preservative

Rosemary Gel

- **Stage 1**

95ml Spring Water

1g/2ml/$\frac{1}{2}$ tsp Xanthan Gum

- **Stage 2**

2ml NFF Moisturiser

8 drops (0.4ml/g) Preservative

20 drops Rosemary Essential Oil

10 drops Lavender Essential Oil

Haemorrhoid Gel

- **Stage 1**

84ml Spring Water

1g/2ml/$\frac{1}{2}$ tsp Xanthan Gum

- **Stage 2**

10ml Witch Hazel Water

3ml Comfrey Glycerol Extract

10 drops (0.5ml/g) Preservative

20 drops Tea Tree Essential Oil

20 drops Cypress Essential Oil

Method for making Gels

1) **Stage 1:** Measure the water in a jug and pour into a bowl.

2) Weigh 1g or measure a level 2ml Measuring spoon with Xanthan Gum Powder.

3) Sprinkle the Xanthan Gum Powder over the water little by little, whisking vigorously. If your Gel gets lumpy, blend until smooth with a stick blender. When there are no more lumps, stop whisking or blending immediately.

4) **Stage 2:** Add all of the pre-measured Stage 2 ingredients and mix in to the Gel. All the Recipes will keep for 1.5-2 years.

Tips for making Gels

- If you prefer your Gel to have a thicker consistency, sprinkle more Xanthan Gum, little by little, into the finished product until you get the consistency you want. Remember to make the Gel of a pourable consistency if you want to bottle it.

- If you want to increase the quantities in the Recipes by 10, simply use 10g of Xanthan Gum. Otherwise use a 2ml Measuring spoon (ten times).

- Don't beat the Xanthan Gum and water so much that the mixture becomes white. Beat hard and fast to remove the lumps and then stop as over-beating makes the Gel go runny.

- If you use the Gels every day, they may have a drying effect on the skin. Add 1-3 % Vegetable Oil to the Gel to counter this as the Vegetable Oil acts as a Fat Restoring Agent in a Gel similar to the effect Omega Fat Restoring Agent has in a Shampoo. **Note:** you can add the

Vegetable Oil to an already-made Gel, simply stir it in briefly (don't overdo it as it will change your Gel to a whitish colour) or you can add the Vegetable Oil the next time you make a Gel.

• If you want to change the colour of the Gel, add Marigold or Carrot CO_2 Extract to make it yellow-orange or Sea Buckthorn CO_2 Extract for an orange colour. Pearlescent Colour (PC) Blue or Green is good for Foot Gel. To use PC Colours, add 1 teaspoon (tsp) of the Colour little by little to 1-2 tablespoons (tbsps) of Glycerine, until you have the Colour you desire. Add to the Gel at Stage 2. Remember to match the Colour you add to the Gel with the Essential Oils that you've used in the product, for e.g. add a blue Colour to a Foot Cream when you've used a cooling Peppermint Essential Oil.

• When adding larger quantities of Essential Oils (over 2%) to Gels, you can reduce the quantity of Preservatives used, especially when adding Aromantic's White Crystal, Tea Tree, or Rosemary Essential Oils (see the Recipes for Gels to see how it's done).

Defining Cellulose Gum and Xanthan Gum

Cellulose Gum INCI name: Cellulose

Cellulose is extracted from plant fibre, primarily from trees, wood pulp and cotton. The different kinds of cellulose-based Gels are often much more stable and better tolerated than other Thickening Agents. Cellulose is used in the food industry and in Skin Care products – in Toothpastes, Aloe Vera Gels, as a stabiliser for Creams, etc. When using Cellulose in your Recipes, you need to have heated the water to around 50°C before sprinkling the Cellulose into it, while whisking constantly until the Gel thickens. Adding up to 4% Cellulose to a Gel Recipe will give it a consistency suitable for use as a Hair Styling Gel. As a food additive, it has the E number, E460-466.

Xanthan Gum INCI name: Xanthan Gum

A wholly natural polysaccharide which is produced by special bacteria – Xanthomonas campestris – through the fermentation of glucose. It is grown under laboratory conditions and no bacteria are left in the finished product. It replaces the gluten in yeast breads and other baking, is widely used in the food industry as Thickener for salad dressings, and is also used as a Thickening Agent in medicines and cosmetics. Its ADI (Acceptable Daily Intake) value is 10mg per kg body weight. You cannot make very thick Gels with Xanthan Gum so it is not suitable for making thick Hair Styling Gels. As a food additive, it has the E number, E415.

Making Ointments & Lip Balms

Ointments

Ointments are used to protect the skin. They are for use on dry, cracked skin and for minor injuries to the skin. To make Ointments you will need a stainless steel saucepan, a bowl, a whisk, a spatula, and a thermometer (optional, up to 100°C) as well as the ingredients.

A simple Base Ointment can be made from Vegetable Oils and Beeswax. The Vegetable Oils nourish the skin while at the same time softening and protecting it. The Beeswax protects the skin while giving the Ointment its consistency. The more Beeswax you add, the harder the Ointment will be and the more Vegetable Oil you add, the softer it will be.

An Ointment has no water in it therefore it needs no Preservative the way Creams do. It does however, benefit from the addition of an antioxidant such as Vitamin E Oil (undiluted).

Recipes for Ointments

Base Ointment

15g Beeswax

85ml Vegetable Oil of your choice (e.g. Sweet Almond Oil*)

*There are many Vegetable Oils to choose from, everything from a simple Olive or Sunflower Oil to a more luxurious Avocado, Apricot Kernel or Peach Kernel Oil.

Method for making Base Ointments

1) Melt the Beeswax and Vegetable Oil together in a double boiler.

2) When the Beeswax is completely melted, remove the bowl or saucepan the ingredients are in from the double boiler.

3) Whisk the Ointment until it has cooled to approximately 40-45°C.

4) Whisk, or stir in, any other ingredients you wish to include.

5) Pour into jars.

How to add heat-sensitive or Vitamin-rich Vegetable Oils "cold" to your Ointment

Once you have some experience of making Ointments, you'll be able to add certain Oils to the Ointment without melting them. You can add up to 50% of the overall Vegetable Oil content of heat-sensitive Oils such as Evening Primrose and Borage, or Vitamin-rich Oils such as Avocado, in your Ointment when the Beeswax has melted. This saves a lot of work heating and cooling the Oils, as well as preserving their nutrients, especially when making large quantities.

1) Slightly adapt the Base Recipe by using 15g Beeswax and 35g Vegetable Oil e.g. Sweet Almond.

2) Follow steps 1 and 2 as described in the Method for making base Ointments.

3) Without waiting for the mixture to cool down, add pre-measured remaining Vegetable Oils "cold", or rather, "room temperature", such as Borage or Avocado Oil.

4) Once the mixture has cooled down to between 45-40°C (NB because it is an Ointment and it will harden, don't wait until the usual 30°C), then add pre-measured (1-5%) Essential Oils of your choice.

5) Lastly, add pre-measured (1-5%) undiluted Vitamin E Oil.

Ointment Recipe Variations

When adding other liquid raw materials, reduce the Vegetable Oils accordingly.

Add at 45-40°C to make the following Ointments:

Arnica Ointment

Add 5ml Arnica Tincture and 1ml Vitamin E Oil (undiluted). **Note:** To avoid the tincture (alcohol-based) from separating from the Ointment, don't add more than 5% of the tincture to the Ointment.

Marigold Ointment (for cracked & dry skin)

Add 2ml/g Marigold CO_2 Extract or 5ml Marigold Tincture and add 1ml Lavender Essential Oil plus 1ml Vitamin E (undiluted).

Liniment (for sore muscles)

Add 3ml Aromantic's White Crystal Blended Essential Oil plus 2ml Vitamin E Oil (undiluted).

Zinc Ointment

Add 4g Zinc Oxide plus 1ml Vitamin E Oil (undiluted). **NB** Do not reduce the Vegetable Oil in this Recipe accordingly!

Foot & Leg Ointment (for tired or cold feet and legs)

Add 3ml Rosemary Oil plus 2ml Vitamin E (undiluted).

Tea Tree Ointment

Add 4ml Tea Tree Essential Oil and 1ml Lavender Essential Oil plus 1ml Vitamin E Oil (undiluted).

St. John's Wort Ointment

Add 30ml St. John's Wort Oil Instead of 30ml Vegetable Oil plus 1ml Vitamin E Oil (undiluted).

Tips for making Ointments

• Ointments are nourishing but also fatty and sticky. You can make them less fatty by reducing the amount of Beeswax and also by using more of the 'dry' feeling Vegetable Oils, such as Thistle and Hemp Seed Oil. Read more about this and about Vegetable Oils versus the petroleum industry's Vaseline and Paraffin Oils in our section on Making Skin & Massage Oils.

Lip Balms

Lips can be sensitive to the effects of the sun, wind, dry air, bacteria and salty foods. They often require a little extra protection. Through the use of natural Fats and Waxes, lips can be cared for without Lip Balms having to be applied over and over again. The need for continual applications can be the result of using Lip Balms containing Vaseline or Paraffin Oil from the petroleum industry.

There are many different Fats, Waxes and Vegetable Oils which can be used to make a Lip Balm base and different Active Ingredients which can be added to create particular kinds of Lip Balms. The Waxes protect the lips while the Vegetable Oils soften them.

The shelf life of the Lip Balms is 1.5-2 years, depending on which Essential Oils you use. e.g. any Citrus Oil will last for 1.5 years but Tea Tree and Lavender Oils will last for 2-3 years.

Recipe for Lip Balms

NB This Recipe doesn't add up to 100g/ml. It is a Recipe for 20x 4.5ml Lip Balm cylinders, therefore make it as accurate as possible.

Base Lip Balm

28g Beeswax

20g Cocoa Butter

50ml Vegetable Oils

1-2ml Essential Oils (25-50 drops*)

*Orange Lemon, Mandarin, Lime, Grapefruit, Spearmint or a small amount of Peppermint. (We use large amounts of Essential Oils to compensate for heat evaporation.)

Note: If you don't have scales buy Aromantic's *Starter Pack No 3 Lip Balms* as it contains pre-measured ingredients for the Base Lip Balm Recipe.

Method for making Lip Balms

1) Heat all the ingredients, except any Essential Oils, in the beaker or stainless steel cup immersed in a pan of hot water (double boiler style).

2) Stir and melt fully.

3) When everything has melted, add up to 25 drops of each Essential Oil (or up to 50 drops of one Oil).

4) Pour into the cylinders up to $^3/_4$ full, allowing it to cool for 10 minutes and shrink slightly. Then, keeping a steady hand, top the cylinders up until full.

5) Leave for a few minutes before putting on the lids.

6) Customise the labels with a felt tip pen and you're ready to sell or give to friends. We suggest a RRP of around £1.00 each for Citrus Lip Balms and £1.50-£1.60 each for a Tea Tree and/or Lavender Lip Balm.

Tip for making Lip Balms

• Always keep the water in the lower half of your double boiler boiling so that you can immerse the beaker in it for reheating the solidified raw materials.

Lip Balm Recipe Variations

Add Value to your Lip Balms by adding other raw materials. Different kinds of Lip Balms can be made through the addition of other fat-soluble ingredients. For every, say 5ml, of any liquid ingredient you add, you will need to remove 5ml of the Vegetable Oil. All of the additional ingredients – apart from Essential Oils – will need to be heated with the main ingredients.

Why not try adding the following raw materials to the Base Lip Balm Recipe:

Lip Balm for Sun Protection

Add Tiosol, 10ml for Sun Protection Factor (SPF) 12, or 5ml for SPF 5-6.

Lip Balm with Zinc

Add 5ml Zinc Oxide (do not reduce the amount of Vegetable Oil).

Tea Tree Lip Balm (for Sore Lips)

Add 1-4ml Tea Tree Oil and up to 1ml Lavender Oil as your Essential Oils.
NB Only use this Lip Balm for treating problems – it should not be used for regular use.

Vitamin Lip Balm

Add 2ml/2g Vitamin E and 5 drops of Carotene.

Read more about Vegetable Oils and Fats in the section *Vegetable Oils for Health & Skin Care products*.

Making Lotions & Sun Creams

Lotions

Lotions are, in principle, runny Creams. Because of their consistency and because they are less fatty than Creams, Lotions are easier to apply to the whole body in order to add moisture and a hint of Fat or Oil to the skin. Lotions contain smaller quantities of Emulsifiers and Vegetable Oils, which are replaced instead by water. Because they are runnier they are usually stored in bottles, however, Lotions are made in the same way as Creams.

They are most often used for special conditions such as rashes, or for areas of the body which get dried out through bathing, such as the hands, feet and elbows. One can also, of course, make Lotions by making Creams runnier (see page 27) where there is a wish to store them in a more hygienic way, which would be to store them in bottles.

Recipes for Lotions

All Recipes make approximately 100ml. The following Lotions are great to use every day or can even be used as After Sun Lotions.

Note: It is difficult to measure small quantities under 5ml accurately. To ease this problem it helps to multiply the recipe.

Soothing Chamomile Lotion

• **Fat Stage (75-80°C)**

3ml Jojoba Oil

2g Shea Butter

0.5g Cetyl Alcohol

1.2g VE Emulsifier

• **Water Stage (75-80°C)**

2g MF Emulsifier

82ml Chamomile Infusion or Still Spring Water

2ml/g Glycerine

12 drops (0.6ml/g) Preservative

• **Third Stage (40-35°C)**

2 ml NFF Moisturiser

1g/ml Chamomile CO_2 Extract

2ml D-Panthenol

1ml/g Vitamin E Oil (undiluted)

10ml Chamomile Flower Water

• **Fourth Stage (30-25°C)**

17 drops Lavender Essential Oil

3 drops Roman Chamomile Essential Oil

Aloe & Avocado Lotion

• Fat Stage (75-80°C)

5ml Avocado Oil

2ml Thistle Oil

0.5g Cetyl Alcohol

1.5g VE Emulsifier

• Water Stage (75-80°C)

2.5g MF Emulsifier

72ml Spring Water (62ml if you are adding the optional 10ml Base Aloe Gel in the Fourth Stage)

4ml/g Glycerine

10 drops (0.5ml/g) Preservative

• Third Stage (40-35°C)

1ml/g Vitamin E Oil (undiluted)

10ml Aloe Vera Concentrate

• Fourth Stage (30-25°C)

20 drops Essential Oil

10ml Base Aloe Gel (optional, but if used remember to only use 62ml of Water in the Water Stage)

Vitamin Lotion

• Fat Stage (75-80°C)

4ml Thistle Oil

2g Shea Butter

0.5g Cetyl Alcohol

1.2g VE Emulsifier

• Water Stage (75-80°C)

2g MF Emulsifier

82.5ml Spring Water

12 drops (0.6ml/g) Preservative

contd/

• Third Stage (40-35°C)

3ml/g Vitamin E (undiluted)

2ml D-Panthenol

1ml/g Vitamin A Palmitate

• Fourth Stage (30-25°C)

20 drops Essential Oil

Carrot Lotion

• Fat Stage (75-80°C)

3ml Thistle Oil

3ml Avocado Oil

0.5g Cetyl Alcohol

1.5g VE Emulsifier

• Water Stage (75-80°C)

2.5g MF Emulsifier

81ml Spring Water

4ml/g Glycerine

12 drops (0.6ml/g) Preservative

• Third Stage (40-35°C)

1ml Carrot CO_2 Extract

2ml/g Vitamin E (undiluted)

2 drops Carotene

• Fourth Stage (30-25°C)

20 drops Essential Oil

Tip for making Lotion

If the Lotion separates, add 0.5-1% Xanthan Gum Powder and whisk in with an electric stick blender.

Basic Method for making all Lotions

Use the Basic Method for making all Creams on page 26. The quantities in the Lotion Recipes will ensure that the resulting product is a Lotion rather than a Cream.

Sun Creams

The Base Cream is for normal to dry skin. Sun Creams with a high Sun Protection Factor (SPF) are possibly too fatty or oily to use on the whole body but are appropriate for use on those areas particularly vulnerable to exposure. It follows from this, then, that low factor Sun Creams are more suitable for more extensive use on the whole body. It is possible to make the Cream slightly runnier if required. In this case, subtract 1g MF Emulsifier and add 1ml more water.

Making Sun Creams with VE/MF Emulsifiers

For the basic method of Making Creams, please see the Recipe for Creams section,

Table 4: Recipes for Sun Creams with varying Sun Protection Factors (SPF)

SPF:	20	10	7	4
Fat Stage (75°-80°C)				
Tiosol (includes Jojoba)	26ml/g	13ml/g	9ml/g	5ml/g
Shea Butter	1g	2g	2g	3g
Sesame Oil		5ml	10ml	13ml
Cetyl Alcohol	1g	1g	1g	1g
VE Emulsifier	3g	3g	3g	3g
Water Stage (75°-80°C)				
MF Emulsifier	5g	5g	5g	5g
Spring Water	58ml	65ml	64ml	64ml
Glycerine	2ml	2ml	2ml	2ml
Cellulose Gum Powder	1g	1g	1g	1g
Preservative	12 drops (0.6ml/g)	12 drops (0.6ml/g)	12 drops (0.6ml/g)	12 drops (0.6ml/g)
Third Stage (40-35°C)				
Vitamin E Oil	1ml/g	1ml/g	1ml/g	1ml/g
D-Panthenol	1ml/g	1ml/g	1ml/g	1ml/g
Fourth Stage (30-25°C)				
Essential Oils	12-15 drops (0.5ml/g)	12-15 drops (0.5ml/g)	12-15 drops (0.5ml/g)	12-15 drops (0.5ml/g)

'Basic Method for making all Creams' on page 26. See Method for Sun Creams with Microfine Titanium Dioxide on page 49 for how to use the Cellulose Gum.

Recipes for Sun Creams

Using the same Method for making all Creams, you can make a Sun Cream by adding different ingredients and quantities to it according to your own liking (see Table 4).

The following Base Sun Creams can be used to make thinner, almost Lotion-like Creams. They contain different quantities of Tiosol (see Table 5 below).

Recipe for Sun Cream with Microfine Titanium Dioxide

(**Note:** the Recipe and Method contains two Fat Stages – this is not a mistake.)

See Table 6 opposite.

Table 5: Recipes for Sun Creams and Lotions

SPF:	5-6 (Cream)	12 (Cream)	5-6 (Lotion)	12 (Lotion)
Fat Stage (75-80°C)				
Tiosol (includes Jojoba)	8ml	16ml	8ml	16ml
Shea Butter	3g	2g	3g	3g
Sesame Oil	1ml	1ml	1ml	1ml
Cetyl Alcohol	1g	2g	0.5g	0.5g
VE Emulsifier	2g	2g	1g	1g
Water Stage (75-80°C)				
MF Emulsifier	3g	3g	2g	2g
Spring Water	75ml	68ml	79ml	70ml
Glycerine	2ml/g	2ml/g	2ml/g	2ml/g
Cellulose Gum Powder	1g	1g	1g	1g
Preservative	12 drops (0.6ml/g)	12 drops (0.6ml/g)	12 drops (0.6ml/g)	12 drops (0.6ml/g)
Third Stage (40-35°C)				
Vitamin E Oil	1ml/g	1ml/g	1ml/g	1ml/g
D-Panthenol	1ml/g	1ml/g	1ml/g	1ml/g
Fourth Stage (30-25°C)				
Essential Oils	12-15 drops (0.5ml/g)	12-15 drops (0.5ml/g)	12-15 drops (0.5ml/g)	12-15 drops (0.5ml/g)

Method for Sun Cream with Microfine Titanium Dioxide

1) **Fat Stage A:** Heat the Fats and Vegetable Oils to over 75°C in a Double Boiler. Then add the pre-measured Microfine Titanium Dioxide Powder, while whisking vigorously so that all the powder is absorbed and dispersed evenly in the liquid. Use a stick blender if you wish.

2) **Fat Stage B:** Add the Cetyl Alcohol & VE Emulsifier, making sure that all of the ingredients are melted properly and that the whole mixture reaches a temperature of 75°C.

3) **Water Stage:** After boiling the Spring Water in a Kettle, measure it according to the Recipe and pour it over the MF Emulsifier and the Glycerine, which you have put into a separate double boiler.

4) Whisk the Water Stage ingredients well together, making sure that the MF Emulsifier powder is fully dissolved in the water and that you don't have any lumps. Then allow the mixture to heat to 75-80°C.

5) When heating the Water Stage to 75-80°C in the double boiler, add the pre-measured Cellulose Gum when whisking or beating it in, until it becomes thickened.

6) When both Fat and Water Stages are over 75°C remove both double boilers from the hob, keeping the Water Stage mixture hot by leaving it on the top half of the double boiler.

7) Now pour the melted Fat Stage into the Water Stage in a thin, steady stream, while continuously whisking the mixture from side to side for 5 minutes. If necessary, use a spatula to scrape the mixture from the sides of the saucepan (or bowl).

Table 6: Recipes for Sun Creams with Microfine Titanium Oxide

SPF:	12-16	15-20
Fat Stage A (75-85°C)		
Sesame Oil	7ml	7ml
Shea Butter	3g	3g
Thistle Oil	10ml	14ml
Microfine Titanium Oxide	8g	10g
Fat Stage A (75-80°C)		
Cetyl Alcohol	1g	1g
VE Emulsifier	3g	3g
Water Stage (75-80°C)		
MF Emulsifier	4g	4g
Boiling Spring Water	54ml	50ml
Glycerine	2ml/g	2ml/g
Cellulose Gum Powder	1g	1g
Preservative	12 drops (0.6ml/g)	12 drops (0.6ml/g)
Third Stage (40-35°C)		
Vitamin E Oil	2ml/g	2ml/g
D-Panthenol	2ml/g	2ml/g
NFF Moisturiser	2ml/g	
Fourth Stage (30-25°C)		
Essential Oils	12-15 drops (0.5ml/g)	12-15 drops (0.5ml/g)

8) Allow the mixture to cool, stirring all the time. You can speed up by the cooling process by replacing the hot water in the double boiler with very COLD water. In the process of cooling

down, the mixture becomes a Cream and will reach its thickest consistency when it is has cooled down to room temperature.

9) **Third Stage:** Stir in the Third Stage ingredients when the mixture has cooled to under 40°C.

10) **Fourth Stage:** Continue stirring until the mixture has cooled to under 25°C, then thoroughly mix in the Essential Oils.

11) Pour the Cream into one big jar or smaller jars and label.

Defining Microfine Titanium Dioxide and Tiosol

Microfine Titanium Dioxide INCI: Titanium Dioxide, Dimethicane

Titanium Dioxide both absorbs and scatters UV radiation. Which process dominates is dependent on the particle size and the wavelength of the incident light beam. Titanium Dioxide primarily absorbs in the UVB range and scatters in the UVA. Microfine Titanium Dioxide, by virtue of its very small particle size, scatters visible (longer wavelength) light poorly. It is because of this that Microfine Titanium Dioxide can appear "transparent" in formulations.

It is accepted as a Sun Screen around the world. This is because it is inorganic and has a record of having no adverse reactions to it. This makes it ideal to use for products used on a daily basis. It can be used in Sun Screens, Moisturisers, Powdered Make-up, Lip and Baby products and virtually any Skin Treatment product. It is also compatible with low pH formulations.

Titanium Dioxide protects against 90% UVA, UVB and UVC radiation.

Table 7: Percentages of Microfine Titanium Oxide to add to products to give them varying SPFs

%	Sun Protection Factor (SPF)
1%	1.5-2
5%	10
10%	15-20

The surface of Microfine Titanium Dioxide is modified to render it extremely hydrophobic, making it a Fat Stage ingredient.

In products you add the Titanium Dioxide to the Fat Stage (without Cetyl Alcohol and VE) when it is over 75°C, whisk it into the heated Oils vigorously. You can also use a stick blender. Then add the Cetyl Alcohol & VE Emulsifier. Make sure that everything is melted and over 75°C.

The better the Titanium Dioxide is dispersed in the product, the higher the SPF. It is therefore important to use a stick blender during the whisking process.

Tiosol INCI: Titanium Dioxide, Cocos Nucifera

Tiosol is a medium for Sun Protection based on old knowledge. It is based on Titanium Dioxide, a natural mineral which, like Zinc Oxide, has been used effectively for sun protection: they both reflect and absorb ultraviolet light. Tiosol protects against UVA, UVB and, to a large degree, UVC rays. It is very easy to use, withstands heating and can attain a Sun Protection Factor of between 2-20. Tiosol consists of 25% Microfine Titanium Dioxide (no nanoparticles) in 75% Organic Jojoba Oil. It is a natural product made with

75% Organic ingredients. Creams with Tiosol and little Fat/Oil have a tendency to become grainy or even to separate. By adding a small quantity of a thickener such as Cellulose Gum Powder this can be prevented and the Creams become lighter and more pleasant to apply to the skin.

Vitamin E Oil and Sun Products

Studies carried out in 1990 show that using a Skin Care product containing 2.5% Vitamin E at the same time as using Sun Care products can increase the Sun Protection Factor (SPF) of that Sun Care product if used for 10 days e.g. the SPF of a commercial Sun Care product was increased from 2 to 4 when the skin was pre-treated for 10 days with a 2.5% Vitamin E Gel.

Making Skin & Massage Oils

For a long time people have used natural Oils and fats for skin, health care and Massage. These cannot be replaced by the synthetic 'Oils' extracted from petroleum (Vaseline and Paraffin). The following comparison explains the reasons for this.

Mineral Oils (Vaseline & Paraffin)

Cannot be absorbed by healthy skin. Create a thin film on the surface of the skin, blocking the pores and preventing the skin from functioning normally. Do not contain any Vitamins and disturb or even stop the skin from being able to absorb fat-soluble Vitamins. Are detrimental to the skin with long-term use. Mineral Oils appear to moisturise the skin but in reality they suppress its normal, healthy functioning. The skin then becomes 'dependent' on constant applications of Mineral Oil which, in turn, result in a deterioration of the skin's character and ability to keep itself healthy. Do not contain any Fatty Acids. Do not go rancid.

Vegetable Fats & Oils

Are readily absorbed by the skin. Are used to nourish (give energy to) the skin and body. Needed to create new cells and for other important processes in the body. Most Vegetable Oils contain Vitamins, which are necessary and good for the skin (such as provitamin A, D, and E). They can stimulate the skin to function better and create better circulation. They soften the skin and make it pliable, helping it to retain its own moisture more effectively. Contain the Essential Fatty Acids. Go rancid after a time. So it is clear from this that Natural Vegetable Oils can actually help the skin to function better. Often they will even help to resolve some of the simpler skin problems, e.g. irritation of the skin caused by Soaps, Cosmetics, clothes or deficiencies in Fats or Vitamins in the skin. Vegetable Oils and Fats consist of Glycerine, Fatty Acids, fat-soluble Vitamins (where applicable) and other Fat soluble ingredients.

The Fatty Acids can also be subdivided into four categories:

> Saturated Fatty Acids
>
> Monounsaturated Fatty Acids
>
> Duounsaturated Fatty acids
>
> Polyunsaturated Fatty Acids

Saturated Fatty Acids

These are solid at room temperature (e.g. Stearic acid) and become a thick liquid inside our bodies. These Fatty Acids are the ones which are supposed to be responsible for vascular and heart disease when consumed in large quantities. They are absorbed slowly by the skin and are added to give Massage and Skin Oils more lubrication. In face

Oils they make the skin's own Oils even oilier. With Oily skin the presence of these Fatty Acids will mean that the pores become more easily blocked which will cause them to enlarge. These Fatty Acids keep well and do not go rancid so quickly. Saturated Fatty Acids are found primarily in Animal Fats such as Lard and Tallow but they are also found in Coconut Butter, Cocoa Butter and Shea Butter.

Monounsaturated Fatty Acids (Omega 9)

These are liquid at room temperature. The most common Monounsaturated Fatty Acids are those Oleic Acids found in most Oils. Oleic Acids keep well.

Duo (Omega 6) and Polyunsaturated (Omega 3) Fatty Acids

Amongst these we find Linoleic (Duo-) and Alpha Linolenic Acid (Poly). Alpha Linolenic Acid is the one most disposed to becoming rancid. They are thin liquids, which are quickly absorbed by the skin. They are 'drier' than the other Fatty Acids. Because they have a tendency to go rancid easily they often need added Vitamin E (as an antioxidant). Duo- and Polyunsaturated Fatty Acids combine with the fats and oils in the skin to make them thinner and help in reducing the size of pores. Therefore they are very important to use for oily skin and skin with large pores. They act like Vitamins for the skin. The most important Fatty Acids are the Essential ones, i.e. Alpha Linolenic and Linoleic Acids, which in some countries are known as Vitamin F. They are called 'Essential' because they are essential to the proper functioning of the skin and indeed the whole body.

Mixing the different Vegetable Oils can create a blend of Oils, which is better suited to the particular purpose for which it is intended than the simple use of one or other Oil. Get to know the different Oils and their characteristics. Test them on your own skin to learn how they feel and how quickly the skin absorbs them. Then try making your own blends, test them in the crook of your arm first to test for any possible allergic reaction and then use on those body parts you have made them for. Store your Vegetable Oils in the fridge. Make up small quantities of your blends so they don't have to stand for too long before being used. Store these at room temperature. Always add a little (0.5%) undiluted Vitamin E to blends of Oils which contain a lot of Polyunsaturated Fatty Acids (Omega 3).

Some examples of Vegetable Oil Blend Recipes

These Recipes make 100ml.

Normal Skin Oil

38ml Jojoba Oil

30ml Sweet Almond Oil

30ml Thistle Oil

2ml/g Vitamin E Oil (undiluted)

Dry and Mature Skin Oil

40ml Apricot Kernel Oil

30ml Macadamia Nut Oil

20ml Thistle Oil

5ml Borage Oil

5ml/g Vitamin E Oil (undiluted)

Oily/Acne Skin Oil

50ml Thistle Oil

28ml Jojoba Oil

20ml Avocado Oil

2ml/g Vitamin A Palmitate

Sensitive Skin Oil

69ml Apricot Kernel Oil

10ml Sweet Almond Oil

10ml Sesame Oil

10ml Shea Butter Oil

1ml/g Vitamin E Oil (undiluted)

Baby Oil

40ml Shea Butter Oil

38ml Avocado Oil

20ml Thistle Oil

2ml/g Vitamin E Oil (undiluted)

Swedish Massage Oil (Blend 1)

33ml Olive Oil

20ml Sweet Almond Oil

15g Coconut Butter (pre-melted)

15ml Jojoba Oil

15ml Apricot Kernel Oil

2ml/g Vitamin E Oil (undiluted)

Swedish Massage Oil (Blend 2)

48ml Sweet Almond Oil

30ml Grape Seed Oil

20ml Shea Butter Oil

2ml/g Vitamin E Oil (undiluted)

Body Oil

40ml Sunflower Oil

30ml Macadamia Nut Oil

27ml Jojoba Oil

3ml/g Vitamin E Oil (undiluted)

Pre-Sun Oil (SPF2)

50ml Jojoba Oil

35ml Sesame Oil

10ml Shea Butter Oil

5ml/g Vitamin E Oil (undiluted)

Method for making the Vegetable Oil Blends

1) Measure all of the Vegetable Oils in the Blend in measuring beaker or cylinder. Add the Vitamins last.

2) Stir together.

3) Pour into a bottle.

4) Secure the cap on the bottle and label.

Adding Essential Oils to Vegetable Oil Blends

Essential Oils can be added to these Blends to enhance their effect. Add approximately 15 drops for Face Oils,

Table 8: Fatty Acid Content and Absorption Note of some common Vegetable Oils

Type of Fatty Acids / Vegetable Oil/Fat	Saturated	Mono unsaturated (Omega 9 & 7)	Duo unsaturated (Omega 6)	Poly unsaturated (Omega 3)	Absorption Note
Chia Seed	11%	7%	21%	63%	Top
Kiwi Seed	8%	12%	15%	65%	Top
Linseed	17%	38%	13%	58%	Top
Camelina	14%	48%	25%	42%	Top
Rosehip Seed	11%	21%	48%	36%	Top
Red Raspberry	4%	11%	56%	32%	Top
Hemp Seed	10%	13%	80%	25%	Top
Evening Primrose	10%	11%	85.5%	1%	Top
Passionflower	14%	19%	74%	5.4%	Top
Borage	14%	31%	62%	≤0.4%	Top
Walnut	11%	20%	65%	14%	Top
Thistle	11%	18.5%	81%	1%	Top
Grape Seed	18%	22%	80%	1%	Top
Sunflower	14%	36.5%	70%	0.5%	Middle
Blackseed	18%	25%	56%	0.2%	Middle
Pumpkin Seed	22%	45%	50%	15%	Middle
Mustard Seed	5%	51%	30%	15%	Middle
Sesame	18.5%	47%	45%	1.5%	Middle
Argan	18%	44%	40%	0%	Middle
Rice Bran	20%	44%	40%	2%	Middle
Avocado	24%	80%	14%	1%	Middle
Hazelnut	10%	85%	19%	1%	Middle
Jojoba	3%	97%	0.3%	0.2%	Middle
Apricot Kernel	9%	69%	34%	0.5%	Middle
Peach Kernel	11.5%	66%	30%	1%	Middle
Almond, Sweet	10%	80%	28%	0.5%	Middle
Sunflower, High Oleic	12%	90%	17%	0%	Middle
Shea Butter Oil	16%	71%	12%	1%	Base

contd/

Olive	22%	86%	9%	1.5%	Base
Macadamia Nut	20.5%	89.5%	5%	2%	Base
Moringa Oil	27%	72%	1.1%	0.2%	Base
Papaya Seed	26%	78%	3.5%	0%	Base
Castor	3%	97%	6%	0%	Base
Neem	40%	54%	16%	0%	Base
Shea Butter	50%	45%	7%	0.5%	Base
Cocoa Butter	65%	34%	3%	0.5%	Base
Palm Kernel Oil/ Butter	83%	15%	2%	0%	Base
Coconut Butter	92%	7%	2%	0%	Base
Coconut Oil, Liquid Fractionated	100%	0%	0%	0%	Base

25-30 drops for Body/Massage Oils. Read more about Vegetable Oils in the section, 'Vegetable Oils for Health & Skin Care Products' on page 12 and about Essential Oils in the chapter dealing with these, which starts on page 73. NB It is difficult to measure small quantities under 5ml/g accurately. To ease this problem it helps to multiply the recipe.

Fatty Acid Content of some Vegetable Oils and Fats

Table 8 shows generally accepted maximum percentages of Fatty Acids that can be found in these Oils and Fats, so totals for each Oil may add up to more than 100%. The Oils and Fats are listed in the order of their Absorption Note i.e. Top, Middle or Base.

Making 2-in-1 Shampoo & Conditioners, Liquid Soaps and Shower Gels

Ingredients commonly used in Shampoos, Liquid Soaps & Shower Gels

It's simple to make your own Shampoos, Liquid Soaps & Shower Gels with our mild and mostly natural ingredients:

Detergents (Alpha, Beta & Sugar)

these are the most important ingredients, as they release the surface tension, loosening oil and dirt. They are mild and kind to the skin and have a gentle cleansing effect.

Fat Restoring Agent (Omega)

redresses the Detergents' drying-out effect, replacing necessary fats to the hair & scalp.

pH Regulating ingredient (Lactic Acid)

adjusts the pH to match the natural pH of the skin to around 5.5-6.

Gelling Agent (Guar Gum)

gives the correct consistency. Guar Gum also acts here as an effective Conditioner.

Preservatives

prevent bacteria, moulds and fungi from developing in the product.

Other ingredients such as Essential Oils, Herbal Infusions, Botanical CO_2 Extracts, Vitamins & Conditioners have a direct effect on the skin and hair.

Base Recipes for 2-in1 Shampoo & Conditioners, Liquid Soaps and Shower Gels

The Recipes shown in Table 9 make 1 litre.

Method for Base 2-in-1 Shampoo & Conditioner Recipes

1) Measure up the Alpha and Sugar or Beta (Detergents) in a jug and then pour into a big heat-resistant bowl. Scrape out as much of the Detergent as possible as it is very thick.

2) Measure up the boiling Water (or the boiling Herbal Infusion or Herbal Decoction) and pour it into the Alpha, Sugar or Beta mixture. Stir it together until it is dissolved.

3) Measure up the Omega, the Guar Gum and the Preservative, and mix well together in a smaller bowl - make sure that there is no Guar Gum powder left around the edges of the bowl. Not doing so may result in lumps in the products.

Table 9: Base Recipes (all recipes make 1 litre)

	Shower Gel	Liquid Soap	Dry Hair 2-in1 Shampoo & Conditioner	Oily Hair 2-in1 Shampoo & Conditioner	Sensitive Scalp/Baby 2-in-1 Shampoo & Conditioner
Alpha	200ml	300ml	200ml	250ml	160ml
Beta	100ml		100ml		70ml
Sugar				50ml	
Omega	30ml/g	30ml/g	30ml/g	10ml/g	30ml/g
Guar Gum			5g	5g	5g
Preservative	5ml/g (100 drops)	5ml/g (100 drops)	5ml/g (100 drops)	5ml/g (100 drops)	5ml/g (100 drops)
Boiling Water	660ml	655ml	657ml	675ml	728ml
Sea Salt		5g			
Lactic Acid	2ml	2ml		2ml	
Essential Oils	60-80 drops	60-80 drops	60-80 drops	60-80 drops	40-50 drops

4) Little by little, pour the Detergent and water mixture from the big bowl into the Omega/Guar Gum blend in the smaller bowl, while stirring continuously. Fill up the smaller bowl and then pour the contents of it all back into the bigger bowl. Stir well together.

5) Place the big bowl in a sink with cold water, stirring the mixture occasionally.

6) When the mixture has cooled to 30°C-25°C, blend in the Essential Oils or other Active Ingredients. If the Shampoo is too thin, stir in Sea Salt little by little until you get the desired consistency.

7) Bottle and label while mixture is still lukewarm.

Method for making Base Shower Gel and Liquid Soap Recipes

1) Measure up the boiling Water (or the boiling Herbal Infusion, Herbal Decoction) and pour it into a big bowl.

2) Measure the Sea Salt (only relevant to Liquid Soap Recipes) and dissolve it into the boiling water in the big bowl.

3) Measure up the Alpha or Beta (Detergents) in a jug and then pour into the big bowl containing the salt and boiling water.

4) Stir the mixture thoroughly until it thickens.

5) Place the big bowl in a sink with cold water, stirring the mixture occasionally.

6) When the mixture has cooled to 30°C-25°C, blend in the Essential Oils or other Active Ingredients. If the product is too thin, stir in more Sea Salt little by little until you get the desired consistency. This works for Shower Gels also.

7) Bottle and label while mixture is still lukewarm.

Shampoo, Shower Gel and Liquid Soap Recipe Variations

Add value to your Shampoos, Shower Gels and Liquid Soaps by customising the Base Recipe to suit different hair types and conditions. Choose effective raw materials, such as Herbal Infusions and Decoctions, Essential Oils, Vitamins, Clays, Moisturisers and other Active Ingredients from Table 10 over. **NB** Don't use all of the ingredients for a certain condition in the same product – select a maximum of three from each category.

Tips for making Shampoos, Shower Gels and Liquid Soaps

• Never use a whisk when using Detergents in a Recipe because it will create a lot of foam and make the mixture difficult to work with.

• If you have any lumps in your mixture, use a strainer to get rid of them.

• Shampoos and Liquid Soaps thicken up gradually until they reach normal room temperature (20°C in Northern Europe).

• If you feel that your Shampoo, Shower Gel or Liquid Soap is too runny, then add Fine Sea Salt little by little and stir until it thickens to a consistency that you're happy with.

• You can add Colours to your Shampoos. The best option from what we stock are the Colours for Water-Based Products (WB). Pearlescent Colours (PC) will fall to the bottom of a bottle because of the Shampoo or Liquid Soap's low viscosity.

• The shelf life of the products made from these Recipes is 2-3 years.

• Using Infusions in your Recipe – if using a Herbal Infusion instead of Boiling Water make it as follows: allow 2-3g Dried Herbs per 100ml water; pour boiling water over the herbs; allow to stand for 10-20 minutes; strain and use according to the Method.

• Using Decoctions in your Recipe - when using Horsetail, or the tougher parts of a plant like the roots, seeds or the bark, make a Decoction rather than an Infusion. Making a Decoction involves boiling the herbs. Put around 2-3g or more of the herb parts into 100ml of water and cover the pot. Bring the mixture to a boil and simmer for about twenty minutes. Steep and strain the mixture and use according to the Method.

• If using a Herbal Infusion or Herbal Decoction instead of Boiling Water, remember to double the amount of Preservative used and reduce the Water volume by the same amount.

• Use 0.8% of Parabens or 1% Preservative K if using a Herbal Infusion or Decoction in your products. Preservative 12 does not work with Detergents.

For more information about using Herbs in Shampoos, see *The Aromantic Guide to the use of Herbs in Skin, Hair and Health Care products.*

Table 10: Different Raw Materials for different Hair and Skin Types and problems

Hair and Skin Type or problem	Herbal Infusion or Decoction	Essential Oils	Active Ingredients
Normal Hair	Chamomile, Lime Blossom	Lavender, Geranium, Ylang Ylang, Rosemary	D-Panthenol, Honey Moisturiser
Dry Hair/Skin	Nettle, Willow Bark, Marigold, Carrageen	Lavender, Rosemary, Sandalwood, Rosewood, Geranium, Ylang Ylang	Jojoba Oil, D-Panthenol, Green Clay, NFF, Kaolin, Borage Oil, Phytokeratin, Honey Moisturiser
Oily Hair/Skin	Nettle, Yarrow, Soapwort Root, Sage, Horsetail	Lavender, Citrus, Rosemary, Cypress, Ylang Ylang, Geranium	D-Panthenol, Green Clay, NFF, Kaolin, Honey-Moisturiser
Lifeless, Sensitive Hair/Sensitive Skin	Horsetail, Coltsfoot, Thyme, Nettles, Marigold	Chamomile, Thyme	D-Panthenol, Sea Silk, Vitamin E Oil, Phytokeratin, Honey Moisturiser
Damaged Hair	Carrageen, Horsetail, Chamomile, Marigold	Chamomile, Sandalwood, Patchouli, Benzoin, Myrrh, Lavender	Aloe Vera, Vitamin E Oil, Phytokeratin, Lecithin, Jojoba Oil, D-Panthenol, Honey Moisturiser
Dandruff	Nettle, Willow Bark, Marigold, Carageen, Rosemary	Cedarwood, Rosemary, Lemon, Lemongrass, Tea Tree	Jojoba Oil, Vitamin E Oil, Honey-Moisturiser
Hair Loss	Nettle, Yarrow, Soapwort Root, Sage, Horsetail, Birch, Rosemary	Rosemary, Ginger, Lavender, Cedarwood, Ylang Ylang, Grapefruit	D-Panthenol, Bio-energiser, Vitamin E Oil, Vitamin A Palmitate, Honey-Moisturiser
Irritation of Scalp/Skin	Marigold, Yarrow, Carageen, Wild Pansy, Witch Hazel, Lady's Mantle, Chamomile, Coltsfoot, Aloe Vera, Horsetail	Ylang Ylang, Tea Tree, Lavender, Chamomile, Sandalwood, Peppermint	D-Panthenol, Vitamin E Oil, Vitamin A Palmitate, Aloe Vera, Honey-Moisturiser, Cosmetic Prebiotic, Comfrey Glycerol Extract

Making Face Masks

Face Masks will contain different ingredients depending on the skin type and purpose for which they are used. You may have spots or bad circulation in the skin or your skin type may need moisturising, or a boost of vitamins and minerals. You may have exposed it to too much sun, or stress, or too little sleep, or you may have been ill or have neglected your skin altogether. Face Masks are ideal to use when your skin needs that extra bit of care. A Face Mask can also be applied to freshen up the skin before going to a party or other event. More and more people are including Face Masks in their daily or weekly beauty routine.

In this chapter we will discuss and make:

Clay Face Masks

Gel Face Masks

Cream Face Masks

Clay Face Masks

The use of Clay Face Masks goes back to ancient times. The Clays that Aromantic stock are sourced from caves in France. They are dried and ionised by the sun and therefore very potent. Clays, in general: are rich in minerals and active enzymes; contract and tone the skin; strengthen the connective tissue; stimulate blood circulation; draw toxins from the skin; and stimulate lymph circulation and thereby more efficient waste handling and boosting of cell nutrients.

Different Clays for different skin types and conditions:

Green Clay

for normal, oily and problem skin

Pink Clay

for dry & sensitive skin

Red Clay

for normal skin

White Clay

for sensitive skin

Yellow Clay

for normal & oily skin

Recipes for Clay Face Masks

These Recipes for Face Masks are based on Clay and water, to which other Active Ingredients may then be added. Apply the Face Mask onto clean skin. **NB** These Recipes make more than 100ml/g.

For a very simple Clay Face Mask:

1) Mix equal amounts of water and Clay.

2) Then add a small quantity of Essential Oil (1-10 drops per 100ml).

3) Apply to the face and wash off after 15 minutes with warm water.

Tips for simple Clay Face Mask

• If you have sensitive skin, a small amount of Vegetable Oil such as Apricot or Peach Kernel can be added to the Recipe, or the Face Mask can be applied to dry skin, which has been covered with a thin layer of Oil. Wash the Face Mask off before it is fully dry. Another alternative is to apply the Face Mask to clean skin, which has been moistened with water. Wash off after 15 minutes.

• If you have normal or oily skin, allow the Face Mask to dry completely (when it starts to crack) before washing off. Grimacing before washing off the Face Mask is an effective way of removing dead skin cells.

NB! Moisten the lips before applying the Face Mask.

Cleansing Clay Mask

• **Stage 1**
7ml Lavender Water
43ml Spring Water
12 drops (0.6ml/g) Preservative
50g Clay powder

• **Stage 2**
3 drops Tea Tree Essential Oil
3 drops Lavender Essential Oil
2 drops Lemon Essential Oil

Stimulating Clay Mask

• **Stage 1**
10ml Peppermint Water
30ml Spring Water
12 drops (0.6ml/g) Preservative
50g Clay

• **Stage 2**
4ml D-Panthenol
5ml Aloe Vera Concentrate
5 drops Lemon Essential Oil
3 drops Peppermint Essential Oil

Nourishing Clay Mask

• **Stage 1**
50ml Rose Water
12 drops (0.6ml/g) Preservative
50g Clay

• **Stage 2**
1.5ml/g Vitamin E (undiluted)
2ml Hemp Seed Oil
5 drops Sandalwood Essential Oil

Clay Mask for Sensitive Skin

• **Stage 1**
6ml Chamomile Water
40ml Spring Water
12 drops (0.6ml/g) Preservative
50g Clay (White or Pink)

• **Stage 2**
6ml Apricot Kernel Oil
1 drop Roman Chamomile Essential Oil (optional)

Method for Face Masks with Clay

1) **Stage 1:** Pour the Water into a bowl and add the drops of Preservative. Sprinkle the pre-measured Clay powder over and allow it to sink into the water without stirring.

2) **Stage 2:** Stirring can begin when the uppermost layer of Clay powder has begun to absorb the water. Add the other ingredients at this point. Mix together well.

3) Finally, spoon into a jar or tub and label.

Tips for making Clay Face Masks

• If your Face Mask product becomes too dry, just add water - especially if it has been stored for more than 1 year.

• The shelf life of these products is approximately 1.5 years. If you want to increase the shelf life, add 0.5% undiluted Vitamin E Oil as an antioxidant.

• Different types of Clay absorb different quantities of liquid so, once you've made your product, you may need to add varying amounts of water and Hydrolates (Herbal or Floral Waters) to it to get the consistency right.

• Aromantic stock many different types of Clay for different skin types.

• By adding more water to the Recipe, you will create more of a Cleanser but remember to add an extra 1 drop of Preservative for every extra 10ml of liquid that you add.

Cream Face Masks

In this section we make two types of Cream Face Masks:

> Cream Face Masks
>
> Moisturising Cream Face Masks

A Cream Face Mask begins with a Base Cream, which becomes a Face Mask with the addition of more active ingredients and Essential Oils than would normally be required for a Cream. Normally the recommended dosage of Essential Oils for a Cream would be 0.5ml but in a Face Mask, this is increased to 1ml. This produces the 'curative' effect that a Face Mask can be designed to have.

The Oil and Fat content provides a matrix for the Essential Oil so that it won't irritate the skin. Normally, if too much active ingredient is added at Stage 3, the Cream will separate and the emulsification (blending) process will fail. Xanthan Gum counteracts this. It helps to bind the active ingredients together and stabilises the emulsification process. Make sure to beat the Xanthan Gum Powder vigorously into the water.

How to use Cream Face Masks: Apply the Face Mask onto clean skin and wash off after 15 minutes.

Recipes for Cream Face Masks

These Recipes make approximately 100ml.

Moisturising Cream Face Mask

• **Fat Stage (75-80°C)**

5ml Castor Oil

4ml Macadamia Nut Oil

1g Shea Butter

1.5g Cetyl Alcohol

2.5g VE Emulsifier

contd over/

- **Water Stage (75-80°C)**

4g MF Emulsifier

64ml Orange Blossom Water or Boiling Spring Water

1g/2ml/$^1/_2$ tsp Xanthan Gum

12 drops (0.6ml/g) Preservative

- **Third Stage (40-35°C)**

5ml NFF Moisturiser

5ml Honey Moisturiser

5ml D-Panthenol

1ml/g Vitamin E Oil (undiluted)

- **Fourth Stage (30-25°C)**

15 drops Lavender Oil

5 drops Geranium Oil

5 drops Clary Sage Oil

Vitamin Cream Face Mask

- **Fat Stage (75-80°C)**

5ml Castor Oil

4ml Avocado Oil

1g Cocoa Butter

1.5g Cetyl Alcohol

2.5g VE Emulsifier

- **Water Stage (75-80°C)**

4g MF Emulsifier

53ml Boiling Still Water or 63ml Marigold Infusion

0.5g/1ml/$^1/_4$ tsp Xanthan Gum

12 drops (0.6ml/g) Preservative (you using the Marigold Infusion, you need to add 1ml/g [20-25 drops] Preservative)

contd/

- **Third Stage (40-35°C)**

10ml Geranium Water if using Still Water in Water Stage

5m/g Vitamin E Oil (undiluted)

2ml/g Vitamin A Palmitate

5ml/g D-Panthenol

5ml Borage Oil or Evening Primrose Oil

- **Fourth Stage (30-25°C)**

15 drops Mandarin Oil

5 drops Ylang Ylang Oil

5 drops Geranium Oil

Method for making Cream Face Masks

1) **Fat Stage:** Heat the Fat Stage ingredients in a double boiler until all of the ingredients have melted and the temperature has risen to 75-80°C. There is no need to use a whisk at this stage.

2) **Water Stage:** After boiling the Spring Water in a Kettle, measure it according to the Recipe and pour it over the MF Emulsifier, which you have put into a separate double boiler.

3) Whisk the Water Stage ingredients well together, making sure that the MF Emulsifier powder is fully dissolved in the water and that you don't have any lumps. Then allow the mixture to heat to 75-80°C.

4) When both Fat and Water Stages are over 75°C, remove both double boilers from the hob, keeping the Water Stage mixture hot by leaving it on the top half of the double boiler.

5) Now pour the melted Fat Stage into the Water Stage in a thin, steady stream, while continuously whisking the mixture from side to side for 5 minutes.

If necessary, use a spatula to scrape the mixture from the sides of the saucepan (or bowl).

6) Allow the mixture to cool, stirring all the time. You can speed up by the cooling process by replacing the hot water in the double boiler with very COLD water. In the process of cooling down, the mixture becomes a Cream and will reach its thickest consistency when it is has cooled down to room temperature.

7) **Third Stage:** Stir in the Third Stage ingredients when the mixture has cooled to under 40°C.

8) **Fourth Stage:** Continue stirring until the mixture has cooled to under 30°C, then thoroughly mix in the Essential Oils.

9) Pour the Cream into one big jar or smaller jars and label.

Gel Face Masks

Xanthan Gum and water are what form the Base for Gel Face Masks. Xanthan Gum is a gelling agent which is easy to use. Xanthan Gum powder is stirred into water, while beating briskly all the time (Stage 1). To this mixture are then added different Active Ingredients, depending on the skin type and purpose for which the Gel Face Mask is being used (Stage 2). See the Recipes section, 'Gels' for more information.

Recipes for Gel Face Masks

How to use the Gel Face Masks: Apply the Face Mask onto clean skin and wash off after 15 minutes.

Rose Gel Mask

A soothing, calming Mask with Rose petal fragrance.

• **Stage 1**

98ml Rose Water

1g/2ml/$\frac{1}{2}$ tsp Xanthan Gum

12 drops (0.6ml/g) Preservative

• **Stage 2**

7 drops Rosewood Essential Oil

7drops Palmarosa Essential Oil

5 drops Geranium Essential Oil

1drops Rose de Mai Absolute (undiluted)

Lavender Gel Mask

A cooling, stimulating Mask, good for soothing sunburnt skin.

• **Stage 1**

74ml Spring Water

1g/2ml/$\frac{1}{2}$ tsp Xanthan Gum

• **Stage 2**

10ml Lavender Water

10ml Aloe Vera Concentrate

2ml St. John's Wort Oil

12 drops (0.6ml/g) Preservative

2ml NFF Moisturiser

10 drops Lavender Essential Oil

1 drop Roman Chamomile Essential Oil

Method for making Gel Face Masks

1) **Stage 1:** Measure the water in a jug and pour into a bowl.

2) Weigh 1g or measure a level 2ml Measuring spoon with Xanthan Gum Powder.

3) Sprinkle the Xanthan Gum Powder over the water little by little, whisking vigorously. If your Gel gets lumpy, blend until smooth with an electric blender.

4) When there are no more lumps, stop whisking or blending. Add the Vegetable Oil in the end.

5) **Stage 2:** Add all of the other pre-measured ingredients and mix well in to the Gel. Spoon into a jar or tub and label.

Tips for making Gel Face Masks

• If you prefer your Gel to have a thicker consistency, sprinkle more Xanthan Gum, little by little, into the finished product until you get the consistency you want. Remember to make the Gel of a pourable consistency if you want to bottle it.

• If you want to increase the quantities in the Recipes x10, simply use 10g of Xanthan Gum. Otherwise use a 2ml Measuring spoon (ten times).

• Don't beat the Xanthan Gum and water so much that the mixture becomes white. Only beat to remove the lumps.

• If you use the Gels every day, they may become dry on the skin. Add 1-3 % Vegetable Oil to the already made Gel to counter this.

• If you want to change the colour of the Gel Face Mask, at Stage 2 add Marigold or Carrot CO_2 Extract to make it yellow-orange or Sea Buckthorn CO_2 Extract for an orange colour. To use Pearlescent Colours, add 1 teaspoon (tsp) of the Colour little by little to 1-2 tablespoons (tbsps) of Glycerine, until you have the Colour you desire. Add to the Gel at Stage 2. Remember to match the Colour you add to the Gel with the Essential Oils that you've used in the product.

Making Anti-Aging & Skin Rejuvenation Products

We would all like to stay forever young and keep our skin like that of a newborn baby, but it is not possible. We can however reduce the skins aging process which starts as soon as we are born when the free radicals start the oxidation (destruction) process of all our connective tissues. We slow this process by using antioxidants like Rosemary Antioxidant CO_2 Extract and Vitamins A, C & E.

What are Antioxidants?

Antioxidants are substances that may protect cells from the damage caused by unstable molecules known as free radicals. Oxygen, an essential element for life, can create damaging by-products during normal cellular metabolism. Antioxidants counteract these cellular by-products, called free radicals, and bind with them before they can cause damage. When Antioxidants perform this cellular repair, or transform the free radicals into non-damaging compounds, they are said to 'scavenge' the free radicals. This is why Antioxidants are known as 'free radical scavengers'.

Normally, the body can handle free radicals, but if Antioxidants are unavailable, or if the free-radical production becomes excessive, damage can occur. Of particular importance is that free radical damage accumulates with age and some studies suggest that free radical damage is the cause of aging. If left unchecked, free radicals may cause heart damage, cancer, cataracts, and a weak immune system.

On the skin level, free radicals damage cells found in the connective tissue such as elastin and collagen. Left untreated, this will cause wrinkles. By applying an Antioxidant through the medium of Creams, Lotions or Oils on the skin every day, this damage can be halted. So, ideally, the best way to protect the skin from aging is to start applying Antioxidants to the skin when we are children!

Recipes for Skin Rejuvenating Toners

Rose Rejuvenating Toner

81ml Rose Water

5ml/g Ginseng Tincture

5ml/g Siberian Ginseng Extract

5ml/g Aloe Vera Concentrate

4ml/g NFF Moisturiser

Neroli Rejuvenating Toner

85ml Neroli (Orange Blossom) Water

6ml/g Aloe Vera Concentrate

2ml/g Sea Silk

3ml/g Hyaluronic Acid

2ml/g Pseudocollagen

2ml/g NFF Moisturiser

Method for making Rejuvenating Toners

Simply measure all of the ingredients and pour into bottles/spray bottles, secure the cap or spray cap, label and use within 6 months. Tip: Add 0.5ml/g Preservative if you want to keep the Toner for more than 6 months.

Recipe for an Anti-Wrinkle/Skin Rejuvenation Cream using Base Emulsifier

This Recipe makes 100-105ml.

Dry/Mature/Sensitive Skin

• **Fat Stage (75-80°C)**

4ml Sunflower Oil

3ml Apricot Kernel

2ml Macadamia Nut Oil

2g Cetyl Alcohol

5ml Base Emulsifier

• **Water Stage (75-80°C)**

56ml Boiling Spring Water

2ml Glycerine

contd/

• **Third Stage (40-35°C)**

3ml Kiwi Seed Oil

4ml/g Vitamin E Oil (undiluted)

1ml/g Vitamin C

2ml/g Hyaluronic Acid

1ml/g Vitamin A Palmitate

2ml/g NFF Moisturiser

2ml/g Remodelling Intense

0.5ml/g Preservative

• **Fourth Stage (35-30°C)**

10-15ml Aloe Vera Gel

• **Fifth Stage (30-25°C)**

12-15 drops Essential Oils

Method for making Anti-Wrinkle/ Skin Rejuvenation Creams

1) **Fat Stage:** Heat the Fat Stage ingredients in a double boiler until all of the ingredients have melted and the temperature has risen to 75-80°C. There is no need to use a whisk at this stage.

2) **Water Stage:** After boiling the Spring Water in a Kettle, measure it according to the Recipe and pour it over the Moisturiser, which you have put into a separate double boiler. Then allow the mixture to heat to 75-80°C.

3) When both Fat and Water Stages are over 75°C, remove both double boilers from the hob, keeping the Water Stage mixture hot by leaving it on the top half of the double boiler.

4) Now pour the melted Water Stage into the Fat Stage in a thin, steady stream, while continuously whisking the mixture from side to side for 5 minutes. If necessary, use a spatula to scrape the mixture from the sides of the saucepan (or bowl).

5) Allow the mixture to cool, stirring all the time. You can speed up by the cooling process by replacing the hot water in the double boiler with very COLD water. In the process of cooling down, the mixture becomes a Cream and will reach its thickest consistency when it is has cooled down to room temperature.

6) **Third Stage:** Stir in the Third Stage ingredients when the mixture has cooled to under 40°C.

7) Add the Preservative.

8) Then add the Aloe Vera Gel until you get the right consistency.

9) **Fourth Stage:** Continue stirring until the mixture has cooled to under 35°C, mix in up to 15ml Aloe Vera Gel (based on 1% Xanthan Gum).

10) **Fifth Stage:** When the mixture has cooled to under 30°C, thoroughly mix in the Essential Oils.

11) Pour the Cream into one big jar or smaller jars and label.

Rejuvenating/Anti-Aging Oil Serums for the Face

You can help reduce the signs of aging in the face and around the eyes by using super potent active raw materials in an Oil Blend called a 'Serum'. A Serum is best applied in the evenings after you have cleansed your face and applied Toner.

Serums prevent premature signs of aging as they contain high doses of antioxidants, which work on the skin if used regularly and thereby reducing damage caused by the aging of the connective tissue such as elastin and collagen.

An Oil Serum will feel dry on the skin as it is usually absorbed quickly by the skin. This is because Oil Serums should contain thin, dry Oils rich in Omega 3 & 6 Essential Fatty Acids combined with Antioxidants. And so important Oils for making Serums are Kiwi Seed, Chia Seed, Camelina, Rosehip Seed, Hemp Seed, Evening Primrose, Borage and Thistle. Serums are used on specific parts of your skin to effect an intensive cure.

Table 11 on the following page shows the ingredients of a range of Extra Intensive Rejuvenating Face Oil Serums for various skin types.

Table 11: Recipes for Extra Intensive Rejuvenating Face Oil Serums

Raw Material	Dry/ Sensitive 1	Dry/ Sensitive 2	Mature Black Skin	Mature/ Sensitive	Sensitive	Sensitive Black Skin	Oily/ Sensitive
Chia Seed Oil		15			10		20
Vit. E Oil	25	30	25	30	25	29	10
Evening Primrose Oil		20		10	10		10
Hemp Seed Oil			10				20
Kiwi Seed Oil	30	30	20	24	32	20	24
Squalane	10		10	10			10
Rosehip Oil	30			10	18	15	
Vit. A Palmitate	1	2	1	1	2	2	2
Macadamia Nut Oil				7			
Avocado Oil			30	5		30	
Remodelling Intense	2	2	2	2	2	2	2
Sea Buckthorn CO_2 Extract	1		1			1	1
Rosemary Antioxidant	10dr	10dr	10dr	10dr	10dr	10dr	10dr
Essential Oils	0.5ml	0.5ml	0.5ml	0.5ml	0.5ml	0.5ml	0.5ml
Total %	100	100	100	100	100	100	100

Making Toothpastes & Mouth Washes

This section contains instructions on how to make 3 different types of Toothpastes plus 2 types of Mouth Wash, each of which can be personalised using different Blends of Essential Oils.

Toothpastes

The purpose of Toothpaste is to cleanse the teeth of residual food particles and other deposits, as well as preventing the build-up of plaque. Most Toothpastes cleanse mechanically through the inclusion of soft minerals, which must be extremely finely ground so that they don't grind or scratch the teeth. These soft minerals are mixed with different substances to create a paste. This can be Glycerine on its own or Glycerine mixed with water plus a substance such as Xanthan Gum, Cellulose Gum, Carrageen, etc, which gives the Toothpaste a good consistency. When adding these, it is possible to make a Toothpaste with fewer soft minerals in it or to make what is known as Tooth Cleanser, which has no soft minerals in it at all. Soft minerals include, amongst others, Chalk, Kaolin and Talcum.

The Toothpaste lather must be mild, neutral and, as far as possible, without taste or smell. The lather has a 'cosmetic' function (Toothpaste is supposed to froth!) But it also has a surface-active effect, which improves the contact between the teeth and the mechanical action of the toothbrush. The lathering content should not be too high and should range from 5-10% (maximum). Sodium Lauryl Sulphate is often used but this is a dusty irritant, which we don't recommend. A better substance to use is Sodium Stearate or Betaine.

To give the Toothpaste a pleasant taste, different Essential Oils, which are also antibacterial, can be added. These leave a refreshing taste in the mouth and kill bacteria. The Oils, which taste good and are suitable, are Spearmint, Peppermint, Menthol, Eucalyptus, Lemon, Orange, Lime, Mandarin, and Sweet Fennel. The stronger antibacterial Oils are Sage, Thyme, Myrrh, Clove (which also anaesthetises) and Tea Tree Oil. Sorbitol can be added as a sweetener. Sorbitol does not affect the teeth (sugar creates cavities). Other safe sweeteners include Xylitol and Saccharine.

If water is added, then a Preservative will need to be added. Colouring can also be added and naturally one would use safe food colouring, such as blue or green.

The most difficult thing about making Toothpaste is getting it mixed together without any lumps and with the soft minerals evenly distributed throughout the paste in such a way that clumps do not occur. This normally requires special mills as used within the industry. At home a large mortar can be used. Good porcelain mortars, (size 1 litre), can be bought from laboratory suppliers.

Recipes for Toothpaste

Basic Toothpaste

50g Chalk

10g Kaolin

1g Sea Salt

39ml Glycerine

15 drops (approximately) Essential Oil

Kaolin Toothpaste

Milder than the Basic Toothpaste, which contains a higher percentage of Chalk.

40g Kaolin

20g Chalk

40ml Glycerine

15 drops (approximately) Essential Oil

Orris Root Toothpaste

10g finely ground Orris Root powder (Iris Florentina)

50g Chalk

40ml (approximately) Glycerine

15 drops (approximately) Essential Oil

Cool Blue Toothpaste with Peppermint

34gr White Clay

15gr Chalk

48gr Glycerine (Add a few drops of Blue Azulene Colour)

2ml Myrrh Tincture

8 drops Peppermint Essential Oil

10 drops Spearmint Essential Oil

2 drops Sage Essential Oil

General method for making Toothpastes

1) Mix all dry ingredients together, add enough Glycerine to make a stiff toothpaste consistency, mixing preferably in a mortar or other bowl, possibly using a food processor.

2) Mix well.

3) Flavour with Essential Oil.

Toothpaste with Thickening/ Gelling Agents I

1) Mix together 2g Cellulose Gum Powder with 20ml Glycerine, ensuring there are no lumps.

2) In a separate bowl, mix together 36g Chalk, 3ml/g Betaine Detergent (lathering agent), 4g Kaolin, 15 drops Essential Oil.

3) Blend step 2 into step 1.

4) Add 35ml Still Spring Water gradually in small quantities & mix in with 10 drops (0.5ml/g) drops Preservative.

Toothpaste with Thickening/Gelling Agents 2

1) Mix together 2g Cellulose Gum with 10ml Glycerine.

2) In a separate bowl, mix together 5g Orris Root, 20g Chalk (finely ground), 15g Kaolin, 5ml/g Betaine Detergent and 15 drops Essential Oil.

3) Blend step 2 into step 1.

4) Add 40ml Still Spring Water gradually in small quantities & mix in with 10 drops (0.5ml/g) drops Preservative.

Toothpaste with Low Abrasive Content

1) Mix together 3g Cellulose Gel with 30ml Glycerine.

2) Mix together 10g Chalk (or Orris Root or Kaolin), 15 drops Essential Oil.

3) Blend step 2 into step 1.

4) Add 56ml Still Spring Water gradually in small quantities & mix in with 10 drops (0.5ml/g) Preservative.

Recommended Herbal Tinctures for Toothpastes

Mix in 2-4% into the final paste:

Tormentilla Root Tincture and Sage Tincture
which are astringent and antibacterial.

Arnica Tincture
for healing inflammation and mouth sores.

Calendula Tincture
for inflammation.

Myrrh Tincture
antibacterial and enhances circulation.

Recommended Essential Oils for Toothpastes

The following blends of Essential Oil Blends can be used in your Toothpastes.

Blend 1
  10 drops Peppermint
  2 drops Sage

Blend 2
  10 drops Peppermint
  2 drops Myrrh

Blend 3
  15 drops Spearmint

Blend 4
  20 drops Tea Tree Oil
  Recipes for Mouth Wash

Mouth Washes

These can be used for many different reasons. The most common is to simply freshen the breath by killing bacteria and preventing the growth of bacteria or fungus. Mouth Wash should be neutral in pH (about 7), taste good, feel good in the mouth and the taste should stay in the mouth for some time.

In these Recipes we use Tinctures with high quantities of tannins and antibacterial properties along with Essential Oils which stimulate the gums and help with gingivitis. Mouth Wash consists of Water, Tinctures, and Essential Oils.

Recipes for Mouth Washes

These Recipes don't always add up to 100ml.

Astringent Mouth Wash

Good for bleeding gums, gum infection and for killing bacteria.

Mix together:

45 ml Tormentilla Root Tincture

15 ml Sage Tincture

15 ml Marigold Tincture

10ml Myrrh Tincture

3 ml Peppermint Essential Oil

3 ml Tea Tree Essential Oil

9 ml Lemon Essential Oil

Healing Mouth Wash

Good for inflammation and healing wounds.

Mix together:

20 ml Marigold Tincture

5 ml Arnica Tincture

3 ml Lemon-scented Tea Tree Essential Oil

1 ml Peppermint Essential Oil

2 drops Myrrh Essential Oil

Freshen-up Mouth Wash

A freshening Mouth Wash.

Mix together:

30 drops Lemon Essential Oil

10 drops Lime Essential Oil

10 drops Peppermint Essential Oil

½ measuring spoon of Menthol crystals

General Method for making and using Mouth Washes

1) Whisk all the ingredients together.

2) Use a few drops in a half glass of water gargle and spit out. **NB!** Do not swallow the Mouth Wash.

Essential Oils & Absolutes: How to Use Them

What are Essential Oils?

Essential Oils are a source of great pleasure and give a sense of well being, both to body and soul. An Essential Oil is a concentrated, aromatic, volatile liquid composed of small oil-like molecules. They consist of a complicated combination of naturally occurring chemicals, which the plant itself produces through photosynthesis. They are called Essential 'Oils' but in fact contain no fatty substances in the same way that, e.g. Almond Oil does. Because they are volatile, they do not create oil stains.

Essential Oil is created in small cavities in the cellular structure of plants, either in the roots, petals, seeds or peel (as in the case of Citrus Oils). The Oil is extracted either by distillation or cold pressing. Essential Oils occur at different levels in different plants, with some plants producing more than others do. For instance, 100kg of petals are required to produce 20ml of Rose Oil, while 100kg of leaves will yield 1-1.5 litres of Peppermint Oil. This means that the cost of Oils will vary but that doesn't make Peppermint Oil less effective than Rose Oil. This section is a brief introduction to the most commonly used ones.

What are Absolutes?

The delicate nature of many flowers means that steam distillation, the usual method of making Essential Oils, cannot be used to extract the Oil because the intense heat destroys the flowers, causing them to become compacted into a solid mass that the steam cannot penetrate.

Therefore, a special process using solvents has been developed to capture the more delicate fragrance without causing any damage to the fragrance. This process does not use any heat or water so none of the water-soluble aromatic compounds are lost the way they are in steam distillation. When an Oil is extracted this way, it is referred to as an Absolute rather than an Essential Oil.

Use of Essential Oils and Absolutes

• To make Natural Perfumes

• To add fragrance to Skin Care and Natural Cosmetic products

• As drops to add to a Vapouriser or for use in a Spraying Flask to create a certain atmosphere, to prevent a cold or simply to freshen the air

• In Baths, Foot Baths, or Hand Baths, e.g. to warm or relax cold limbs or, when slightly colder water is used, to create a stimulating effect

• In Compresses e.g. to cool sunburn

• In Massage and other Skin Care Oils e.g. to increase blood circulation

• To inhale directly from the bottle, from a Vapouriser, or to use in a Facial Steam Bath e.g. to aid relaxation or to clear congested air passages.

Safety Guidelines for using Essential Oils and Absolutes

When using Essential Oils and Absolutes it is very important to adhere to the recommended dosage to achieve the desired effect. The wrong dosage (there is often the temptation to use too much) can result in skin damage, headache, nausea or similar. Some Essential Oils and Absolutes are not suitable for use during pregnancy or in conjunction with high blood pressure, while some should be used sparingly on the skin. (See directions for individual Oils).

Remember that if you are not a qualified Aromatherapist, you should always consult a qualified practitioner or consult a recommended reference book before using Essential Oils and Absolutes.

Properties of some commonly used Essential Oils

Bay Leaf

Latin name: Laurus nobilis

Parts used: leaves

Perfume: Herbaceous, round, green aroma, smelling of the woods and slightly minty.

Skin care: Antiseptic, good for oily skin and acne. Strengthens hair.

Vapouriser: Mood stabiliser, increases self-confidence, uplifting and relaxing.

Safety: Do not use when pregnant.

Benzoin

Latin name: Styrax tonkinensis

Parts used: resin

Perfume: Warm, well-rounded, soft aroma with a touch of vanilla.

Skin care: Chapped and cracked skin.

Vapouriser: Warming and comforting in difficult circumstances, good for sadness and loneliness. Relaxing. Gives a cosy aroma when used in combination e.g. with Orange and Lavender.

Safety: Can be irritating to the skin in high doses.

Bergamot

Latin name: Citrus bergamia

Parts used: peel

Perfume: Sweet citrus aroma with a floral/fruity undertone.

Skin care: Good for oily skin and acne.

Vapouriser: Uplifting, increases self-confidence, good for stress relief.

Safety: Increases the skin's sensitivity to sunlight.

Cedarwood

Latin name: Cedrus atlantica

Parts used: wood

Perfume: Soft, round, sweet, woody, resiny aroma.

Skin care: Astringent on oily skin, antiseptic with acne.

Vapouriser: Relaxing, harmonising, helps one to focus and to find integrity. Good Oil for meditation.

Safety: Do not use when pregnant.

Clove

Latin name: Eugenia caryophyllus

Parts used: flowers/ buds

Perfume: Deep, very warm and spicy aroma. Good for men's perfumes.

Skin care: Not commonly used for treating acne but can be used for this purpose.

Vapouriser: Warming, stimulating effect. Very antiseptic.

Safety: Very irritating to the skin. Must be used in concentrations of less than 1% in Vegetable Oil and even less in other products. Do not use in Baths.

Cypress

Latin name: Cupressus sempervirens

Parts used: needles

Perfume: Smell of needles, with a herbaceous, woody, resinous tone.

Skin Care: Astringent, good for oily skin and skin with broken capillaries. Good for cellulite - tightens up the skin, diuretic.

Vapouriser: For those who need structure in their lives or for those who need to depend on themselves in difficult situations.

Geranium

Latin name: Pelargonium graveolens

Parts used: leaves

Perfume: Mixture of rose and citrus aroma, quite direct and slightly green.

Skin Care: Regulates production of sebum (oil from glands in the skin). Good for oily and dry skin. For treating cellulite - stimulates the lymphatic system.

Vapouriser: Uplifting, stabilising, combats stress and mood swings.

Grapefruit

Latin name: Citrus paradisi

Parts used: peel

Perfume: Slightly sour but refreshing citrus aroma with a bitter touch.

Skin care: Good for oily skin and acne. Helps to break down cellulite. Stimulates hair growth. Vapouriser: Mentally refreshing.

Safety: Increases the skin's sensitivity to sunlight.

Jasmine (Absolute)

Latin name: Jasmin grandifolium

Parts used: flowers

Perfume: Hypnotically sweet, floral aroma with a hint of green and herbs. Be careful with dosage, as it can be very dominant.

Skin care: Good for sensitive and very dry skin.

Vapouriser: Uplifting, euphoric, warming; helps in the release of feelings, is aphrodisiac, good for clearing apathy.

Safety: Dose with care. Can be suffocating and irritating to the skin if dosage is too high. Do not use if pregnant.

Lavender

Latin name: Lavandula angustifolia

Parts used: flowers

Perfume: Typical lavender aroma, floral, herbaceous and green.

Skin care: Good for all skin types including mature, sunburnt and irritated skin and skin with acne. Acts as an effective synergist to many other Oils.

Vapouriser: Relaxing, good for stress relief, tension and nervousness. Harmonises and stabilises, good for nightmares.

Lemon

Latin name: Citrus limonum

Parts used: peel

Perfume: Fresh, sweet and sour citrus aroma with a touch of green.

Skin care: Good for oily skin and acne. Helps to break down cellulite.

Vapouriser: Cleansing, slightly cooling and refreshing. Use when confused, indecisive or irritable. Increases concentration. Antiseptic.

Safety: Increases the skin's sensitivity to sunlight.

Mandarin

Latin name: Citrus reticulata

Parts used: peel

Perfume: Soft, warm, kind citrus aroma with slightly floral fragrance.

Skin care: Skin toner, good for all skin types.

Vapouriser: Gently refreshing, full of care and delight. Gentle and effective for children and elderly.

Neroli

Latin name: Citrus aurantium

Parts used: flowers

Perfume: Very warm, floral and slightly fruity aroma

Skin care: Mature skin, broken capillaries, sensitive and dry skin. Tones the skin.

Vapouriser: Good for restlessness, anxiety and shock. Soothing where there is sorrow or fear. Relaxing and uplifting.

Orange

Latin name: Citrus sinensis

Parts used: peel

Perfume: Sweet, warm, citrus. Goes well with most other fragrances.

Skin care: For mature skin, swollen skin or acne. Good in Foot Creams for dissolving hard skin. Brightens dull and oily skin.

Vapouriser: Uplifting, relaxing, creates a sunny, warm disposition, good for tension and stress relief.

Patchouli

Latin name: Pogostemon patchouli

Parts used: leaves

Perfume: Earthy, soft aroma with a with a rich, herbaceous touch.

Skin care: Astringent. Use for chapped and cracked skin, oily and mature skin. Tightens up tired, loose skin. Combats wrinkles and large pores.

Vapouriser: Aphrodisiac, grounding, stabilising effect whilst effectively taking the weight off the shoulders.

Petitgrain

Latin name: Citrus aurantium

Parts used: leaves

Perfume: Warm, slightly over-ripe citrus aroma with a hint of flowers.

Skin care: Oily and dry skin, acne. Skin toner.

Vapouriser: Good for stress relief.

Peppermint

Latin name: Mentha piperita

Parts used: leaves.

Perfume: Cooling, direct, lively, invigorating scent. Be careful with dosage as it can be very dominant.

Skin care: Cooling, refreshing.

Vapouriser: Cooling, refreshing, good for tiredness and to extend concentration.

Safety: Use with care. Can cause itching when used in concentrations higher than 1%. Only 1 drop is recommended for use in one Baths. Do not use in conjunction with homoeopathic remedies as it can act as an antidote.

Rose de Mai (Absolute)

Latin name: Rosa centifolia

Parts used: flowers

Perfume: As rose should be, very floral, slightly citrus and spicy.

Skin care: Good for dry and mature skin as well as broken capillaries.

Vapouriser: Aphrodisiac, good for stress relief, strengthens femininity.

Rosemary

Latin name: Rosmarinus officinalis

Parts used: leaves

Perfume: Herbaceous, spicy, stimulating, minty aroma. Be careful with dosing, as it can be very dominant.

Skin care: Good for bad circulation in the skin and cellulite. Warming. Good for oily skin and acne as well as small

amounts of dry and mature skin. Strengthens hair.

Vapouriser: Stimulating, invigorating, refreshing. Good for memory and concentration, for apathy and indecisiveness.

Safety: Do not use when pregnant or at the same time as homoeopathic treatment. Use with care where there is high blood pressure. Do not use if epileptic.

Sandalwood Mysore/Sandalwood Caledonia

Latin name: Santalum album/ Santalum austrocaledonicum Viell.

Parts used: wood

Perfume: Sweet, warm, woody smell.

Skin care: Good for dry and sensitive skin. Antiseptic for acne.

Vapouriser: Relaxing, harmonising, gives a feeling of sensuality. Aphrodisiac. Stabilises and protects where there is fear. A good Oil for meditation.

Tea Tree

Latin name: Melaleuca alternifolia

Parts used: leaves.

Perfume: Cleansing, herbaceous and slightly woody aroma.

Skin care: Use for acne, sunburn, fungal infections, psoriasis, sweaty feet, insect bites etc.

Vapouriser: Room cleansing.

Vetivert

Latin name: Vetiveria zizanoides

Parts used: root.

Perfume: Juicy, earthy, smoky aroma with a sweet undertone. Good for men's Eau de Colognes.

Table 12

	Face & Skin Cream	Sport/ Massage Cream	Face & Skin Gel	Sport Massage Oil	Face & Skin Massage Oil	Massage Oil	Fragrance Burner	Spray Flask	One Bath
Max. dosage for mixtures	1.0%	2.5%	1%	2%	1.5%	3%	10 dr	2.5%	6 dr
Bay Leaf	0.5%	1%	0.25%	1%	0.5%	1.5%	10 dr	1%	2 dr
Benzoin	0.5%	1%	0.5%	1%	0.75%	1%	6 dr	1%	2 dr
Bergamot	0.5%	1%	1%	1.5%	1.5%	2%	10 dr	2%	2 dr
Cedarwood	0.75%	1%	1%	2%	1%	2%	6 dr	1%	3 dr
Clove	0.2%	0.5%	0.1%	0.2%	0.25%	0.75%	3 dr	0.5%	X
Cypress	0.75%	1%	0.75%	2%	1.5%	3%	14 dr	2%	4 dr
Geranium	0.75%	1%	0.75%	2%	1.5%	2%	10 dr	1%	3 dr
Grapefruit	0.75%	1%	1%	1.5%	1.5%	2%	10 dr	2%	3 dr
Jasmine (absolute)*	0.75%	1%	1%	1%			14 dr	1%	3 dr
Lavender	0.75%	2%	1.5%	3%	1.5%	3%	9 dr	2.5%	6 dr
Lemon	0.75%	0.5%	1%	1.5%	1.5%	2%	14 dr	2.5%	3 dr
Mandarin	0.75%	1%	1%	1.5%	1.5%	2%	9 dr	2%	4 dr
Neroli *	0.75%	3%	1%	2%			14 dr	1%	6 dr
Orange	0.75%	1%	1%	1%	1.5%	3%	9 dr	2%	3 dr
Patchouli	0.75%	1%	1.5%	1%	1%	1.5%	5 dr	1%	3 dr
Peppermint	0.25%	0.75%	0.25%	0.75%	0.5%	1%	6 dr	1%	1 dr
Petitgrain	0.75%	1%	1%	2%	1.5%	3%	6 dr	1.5%	6 dr
Rose (absolute)*	0.75%	3%	2%	1%			13 dr	1%	6 dr
Rosemary	0.75%	1%	0.5%	2%	0.5%	2.5%	5 dr	1%	3 dr
Sandalwood	0.75%	1%	1%	2%	1%	2%	5 dr	1%	3 dr
Tea Tree	1.5%	3%	1.5%	3%	1.5%	3%	9 dr	2.5%	6 dr
Vetivert	0.5%	1%	1%	1.5%	1%	3%	5 dr	0.5%	3 dr
Ylang Ylang	0.5%	1%	0.75%	1.5%	1%	2%	5 dr	1%	3 dr

dr = drops   **Diluted in 9 parts alcohol*

Skin care: Good for mature skin, astringent and softening with chapped and cracked skin.

Vapouriser: Good for those who need grounding or who lack security. Deeply relaxing. Strengthens the nervous system.

Ylang-Ylang

Latin name: Cananga odorata genuina

Parts used: flowers

Perfume: Floral, exotic, slightly banana scented, narcotic aroma.

Skin care: Stabilises production of sebum (oil from glands in the skin), good for oily skin and acne. Classic hair Oil in Asia.

Vapouriser: Aphrodisiac, uplifting, relaxing, good for anger, restlessness & stress.

Percentages Related to droppers (for Essential Oil bottles)

The size of the drops depends on the lining in the neck of the small bottle containing your Essential Oil. This regulates the size of drops individually dispensed from the bottle.

Smaller Droppers

Most Essential Oils are thin and require a smaller dropper where percentage dosing is as follows:

0.1% = 2 drops per 100ml

0.2% = 4 drops per 100ml

0.25% = 6 drops per 100ml

0.5% = 12 drops per 100ml

0.75% = 18 drops per 100ml

1% = 25 drops per 100ml

1.5% = 32 drops per 100ml

2% = 50 drops per 100ml

2.5% = 62 drops per 100ml

3% = 75 drops per 100ml

4% = 100 drops per 100ml

Larger Droppers

Vetivert, Sandalwood and Benzoin are thicker Oils and require a larger dropper, which releases larger drops. Percentage dosing for these Oils will be:

1% = 10 drops per 100ml

2% = 20 drops per 100ml

2.5% = 25 drops per 100ml

3% = 30 drops per 100ml

4% = 40 drops per 100ml

Making Natural Perfumes based on using only Essential Oils

The word *perfume* comes from the Latin *per fumum*, meaning 'through smoke'. Traditionally, the Catholic Church, native peoples and shamans burn different parts of plants and resins which then, through the agency of the smoke, give off their fragrance. The development of scent and perfume making goes forward, for better or for worse.

The beginning of the 1900s saw the development of industrially produced synthetic components for perfumes and today nearly all perfumes on the market will contain a percentage of synthetically produced fragrances. However, an increase in the demand for natural products has also increased the demand for naturally produced fragrances and, in particular, Perfumes.

An Enjoyable Hobby

Making your own Perfume with Essential Oils is exciting and is made possible through Nature's fantastic, rich, variety of fragrances. Not only that, it is also fun. You can create a Perfume which is entirely yours. It can consist mainly of your favourite Essential Oil or of Oils chosen to produce a particular effect, e.g. relaxation, stimulation, or feelings of happiness, courage, creativity or eroticism. A Perfume is nearly always made up of a mixture of top, middle and base 'Notes'. When creating a Perfume one should therefore always use a selection of Oils from all three categories.

Balancing Your Perfume

Even though you may not feel drawn to the lighter, fresher scents you should always include some Essential Oils from the Top Note range to ensure a balanced Perfume. Similarly, even though you may not feel drawn to the heavier scents, you should include some Oils from the Base Note range so the perfume doesn't evaporate too quickly and to give it consistency.

Top Note

Consists of Essential Oils, which create feelings of freshness and vigour. They tend to be very volatile and the first to evaporate from Perfume. Top Note Oils are usually extracted from Citrus fruit. Essential Oils classified as Top Note include: Bergamot, Grapefruit, Lemon, Mandarin, Orange, Peppermint, Petitgrain.

Middle Note

Consists of Oils, which give substance and heart to a Perfume and are often those which there are most of in a Perfume. Middle Note Oils are usually extracted from flowers and leaves. Essential Oils classified as Middle Note include: Bay Leaf, Cloves, Cypress, Geranium, Jasmine (Absolute), Lavender, Neroli, Rose de Mai (Absolute), Rosemary, Rosewood, Tea Tree, Ylang Ylang.

Base Note

Consists of Oils which leave the skin, and Perfume, last. They give the Perfume weight and consistency and bind the Top and Middle Note range Oils so they don't evaporate too quickly. Base Note Oils are usually extracted from woody stems and roots. Essential Oils classified as Base Notes include: Benzoin, Cedarwood, Patchouli, Sandalwood, Vetivert.

Fragrance Note

Essential Oils can also be classified according to how they smell, e.g. rosy or minty. This method of classification has nothing to do with which part of the plant the Oil comes from but rather with how the Oil smells. If you want a lot of Floral and Root Notes in your Perfume you can use a predominance of these but do consider using some Citrus notes so as to include a Top Note. Sometimes the difference between Woody and Herbaceous or Spicy and Herbaceous Notes can be hard to define. You may also have your own ideas, which differ from what we are suggesting here. It is naturally up to you and what you think, as the creator of your own Perfume, that is most important.

Woody Notes

Cedarwood, Cypress, Sandalwood, Tea Tree

Root Notes

Benzoin, Patchouli, Vetivert

Citrus Notes

Bergamot, Grapefruit, Lemon, Mandarin, Orange

Spicy Notes

Bay Leaf, Cloves

Rosy Notes

Geranium, Rose de Mai (Absolute), Rosewood

Orange Notes

Neroli, Petitgrain

Herbaceous Notes: Lavender, Rosemary

Floral Note

Jasmine (Absolute), Ylang Ylang

Minty Notes

Peppermint

Method for making Perfumes

1) The number of drops indicated is for a 100% Perfume mixture, which is the concentrate you will need to make Eau de Parfum, Eau de Toilette or Eau de Cologne. You then add a carrier, e.g. Alcohol, in different quantities, depending on which of type of Perfume you are making.

2) Pour the desired amount of Alcohol (at 96% strength) into a small cup and add the Essential Oils you want to have in your Perfume. Mix together, pour into a bottle and allow to mature for at least 3 weeks.

NB High alcohol content – at least 80% – Polish Vodka from the off-licence or supermarket can be used if you can't find 96% strength.

Eau de Parfum

2ml alcohol + approximately 40-60 drops of Essential Oil

Eau de Toilette

6ml alcohol + approximately 40-60 drops of Essential Oils

Eau de Cologne

10ml alcohol + approximately 40-60 drops of Essential Oils

Recipes for Natural Perfumes using Essential Oils

These are Recipes for Perfume concentrates of approximately 50 drops ('*' = Diluted Essential Oils that are diluted in 9 parts alcohol.)

Exotic Flower

• **Top Note**
Grapefruit (10 drops)
Lemon (10 drops)
Orange (8 drops)

• **Middle Note**
Cloves (2 drops)
Ylang Ylang (8 drops)
Jasmine* (5 drops)

• **Base Note**
Patchouli (5 drops)
Benzoin (2 drops)

Petit Fleur

• **Top Note**
Mandarin (20 drops)

• **Middle Note**
Ylang Ylang (10 drops)
Rose de Mai* (10 drops)

• **Base Note**
Sandalwood (10 drops)

Sunshine

• **Top Note**
Mandarin (11 drops)
Orange (11 drops)
Petitgrain (6 drops)

• **Middle Note**
Rose de Mai* (2 drops)
Jasmine* (2 drops)
Neroli* (8 drops)

• **Base Note**
Sandalwood (4 drops)
Benzoin (6 drops)

Bright Day

• **Top Note**
Lemon (20 drops)

• **Middle Note**
Jasmine* (8 drops)
Neroli* (13 drops)

• **Base Note**
Sandalwood (4 drops)
Benzoin (5 drops)

Stimulating

• **Top Note**
Lemon (11 drops)
Grapefruit (11 drops)
Peppermint (5 drops)

• **Middle Note**
Tea Tree (5 drops)

contd over/

Rosemary (6 drops)

Geranium (2 drops)

Clove (2 drops)

Ylang Ylang (5 drops)

- **Base Note**

Patchouli (3 drops)

Bouquet de Herbs

- **Top Note**

Lemon (13 drops)

Bergamot (13 drops)

Mandarin (5 drops)

- **Middle Note**

Lavender (5 drops)

Rosemary (3 drops)

Cypress (4 drops)

Bay Leaf (2 drops)

Jasmine* (1 drops)

- **Base Note**

Vetivert (1 drops)

Cedarwood (3 drops)

Parfum de Luxe

- **Top Note**

Mandarin (11 drops)

Grapefruit (11 drops)

Bergamot (10 drops)

- **Middle Note**

Rose de Mai* (3 drops)

Jasmine* (3 drops)

Neroli* (4 drops)

- **Base Note**

Sandalwood (4 drops)

Benzoin (4 drops)

Petit Lemon

- **Top Note**

Lemon (24 drops)

- **Middle Note**

Rosewood (13 drops)

Neroli* (10 drops)

- **Base Note**

Vetivert (3 drops)

Young Flower

- **Top Note**

Orange (8 drops)

Bergamot (8 drops)

- **Middle Note**

Rose de Mai* (10 drops)

Geranium (6 drops)

Neroli* (9 drops)

- **Base Note**

Patchouli (2 drops)

Sandalwood (7 drops)

Petite Lavande

- **Top Note**

Bergamot (20 drops)

- **Middle Note**

Lavender (20 drops)

Jasmine* (3 drops)

Neroli* (4 drops)

- **Base Note**

Benzoin (3 drops)

Relaxing Perfume

• **Top Note**
Petitgrain (5 drops)
Mandarin (10 drops)
Orange (5 drops)

• **Middle Note**
Lavender (5 drops)
Ylang Ylang (7 drops)
Geranium (5 drops)

• **Base Note**
Vetivert (3 drops)
Cedarwood (5 drops)
Sandalwood (5 drops)

Night Roses

• **Top Note**
Petitgrain (9 drops)
Grapefruit (5 drops)

• **Middle Note**
Rosewood (5 drops)
Rose de Mai* (10 drops)
Geranium (3 drops)
Lavender (3 drops)

• **Base Note**
Sandalwood (8 drops)
Benzoin (5 drops)
Cedarwood (2 drops)

Adding Fragrances to Creams & other Skin Care products

The fragrance of a Skin Care product affects the way we experience it. The smell of a product is very important. If we are not attracted by the product's smell then we will quite simply not be drawn to the Cream itself either. When we buy Skin Care products we do so very much guided by our noses and our sense of smell.

Artificially Synthesised Scents

Occur in nearly all Skin Care products currently sold in shops, department stores, perfumeries, clothes shops etc. – and, strangely enough, a lot of what you buy in Health Food shops also contain artificially synthesised scents. No matter how good a Skin Care product smells, and because of this, how good we think it may be for our skin, these synthetic scents can cause skin problems. Nor do they offer any therapeutic benefits to our skin. Their only reason for being there is to appeal to our sense of smell and to conceal the original fragrance of the product.

Using Essential Oils and Absolutes in Skin Care products

Essential Oils and Absolutes, through our sense of smell, create an experience of well being, which affects us mentally as well as emotionally while at the same time having a positive effect on the condition of our skin. Using Essential Oils and Absolutes, you can add your own chosen fragrance to your Natural Creams and Gels yourself. Compose the fragrance of your Creams and Gels according to the effect you would like it to have, your skin type or whatever skin problem you may have, and not least of all, according to the scent which you find most attractive. You can even add different fragrances to the whole family's Shower Gels and Shampoos.

When adding scent to Skin Care products, you need to consider which products are the best to add Essential Oils and Absolutes to. In general, because Fats are the best medium for binding Essential Oils and Absolutes without creating irritation to the skin, you can add more Essential Oil and Absolutes to Creams than to Gels. This is important particularly for preparations that are used for longer periods, such as all day. On the other hand, with Gel-based Face Masks, which will only be used for a few minutes you can be more generous when adding your drops of Essential Oil and Absolutes.

Also, dose carefully if you have oily skin so it doesn't become dry instead. Add some of those Essential Oils and Absolutes that help to regulate sebum production.

Different Skin Types and Conditions

Dry Skin

is skin that needs both oils and moisture. To balance oil production (sebum regulation) in the skin use Geranium, Lavender and Ylang Ylang. To balance moisture content, use the Essential Oils of Lavender, Neroli and Sandalwood and the Absolutes of Rose and Jasmine.

Oily Skin

produces a lot of sebum. Sebum-regulating Essential Oils are the same as those for regulating oil production in Dry Skin and are used to achieve a normal, balanced skin. You can also use Essential Oils that have a drying effect, such as Lemon, Rosemary and Cypress.

Acne

consists of blocked pores, which become infected, producing spots. Sebum regulating Oils work well here. To disinfect the skin, use Tea Tree, Lemon and Bergamot. To prevent infection, use Tea Tree, Jasmine Absolute and Lavender. Cleansing Essential Oils are Lavender, Rosemary, Tea Tree and Lemon.

Sensitive Skin

reacts both to internal as well as external factors, such as weather, wind, the wrong Skin Care products, food and anxiety. When using Essential Oils and Absolutes on very sensitive skin you should be very careful with dosages. Use 1-3 drops to 30ml of Cream. Stick to the Recipes until you have become familiar with the Oils' strength and effects.

Mature Skin

begins to occur after the age of 40. The skin begins to lose its elasticity and there will be more or less sharp lines around the eyes, mouth and on the forehead. If the skin is not too sensitive you can use Rosemary to increase the blood circulation in the skin. Mandarin increases elasticity and tones up loose skin. Lavender and Rosewood stimulate cell regeneration so that fine, new skin comes to the surface.

Large Pores

are inherited but can be modified through the use of good products. Lemon, Cedarwood, Geranium and Cypress are astringent Oils, which help to contract and strengthen the skin.

Broken Capillaries

are hard to cure but through regular treatment you can strengthen the capillaries so they become smaller and less visible. The Oils to use are Cypress, Rose and Neroli.

Essential Oil and Absolute Blends for Creams

NB We use Neroli Essential Oil and Jasmine and Rose Absolutes diluted in alcohol so that you can add them to 15ml Jars without overpowering the other Oils. If you are making large quantities, you can use approximately $\frac{1}{10}$th of the pure Oils instead.

Essential Oil Blends for Gels

Aloe Vera Gels usually contain no Fats and therefore do not nourish the skin in any way. However, they are good for protection e.g. after shaving or to cool the skin e.g. after sunburn. Gels work well as carriers for Essential Oils and combined together with e.g. Peppermint can make a Massage Gel which is good for tired or hot feet, or for making a Moisturising Mask.

Table 13: Essential Oil and Absolute Blends for Creams

		15ml	30ml
		no. of drops	
Dry Skin 1	Orange	2	4
	Rosewood	2	3
	Lavender	2	3
	Benzoin	1	1
Dry Skin 2	Mandarin	2	4
	Neroli*	2	3
	Jasmine Abs*	1	2
	Sandalwood	1	2
Dry Skin 3	Petitgrain	1	2
	Lavender	2	4
	Geranium	1	2
	Patchouli	1	2
Oily Skin 1	Lemon	2	4
	Cypress	2	4
	Ylang Ylang	1	2
	Sandalwood	1	1
Oily Skin 2	Grapefruit	2	4
	Ylang Ylang	1	1
	Lavender	2	4
	Cedarwood	1	2
Oily Skin 3	Bergamot	2	4
	Rosemary	2	3
	Bay Leaf	1	2
	Patchouli	1	2
Acne 1	Grapefruit	1	2
	Tea Tree	3	6
	Ylang Ylang	1	1
	Sandalwood	1	2
Acne 2	Lemon	1	2
	Lavender	2	4
	Tea Tree	3	6
	Cedarwood	1	1
Acne 3	Bergamot	2	4
	Geranium	1	2
	Rosemary	2	3
	Patchouli	1	2
Mature Skin 1	Petitgrain	1	2
	Rose de Mai Abs*	2	4
	Lavender	2	4
	Vetivert	1	1
Mature Skin 2	Mandarin	1	2
	Rosemary	1	2
	Ylang Ylang	1	2
	Sandalwood	3	5
Mature Skin 3	Orange	1	2
	Ylang Ylang	1	2
	Geranium	2	3
	Patchouli	1	2
Broken Capillaries	Mandarin	1	2
	Cypress	2	3
	Rose de Mai Abs*	2	3
	Cedarwood	1	1
Sensitive Skin	Mandarin	1	2
	Lavender	1	2
	Neroli*	1	1
	Sandalwood	1	1
Warming Foot Cream	Rosemary	6	12
	Lavender	6	12
	Benzoin	2	4
Soothing 'After Sun'	Lavender	3	6
	Rosemary	2	4
	Sandalwood	2	3

*Diluted in 9 parts alcohol

Table 14: Essential Oil Blends for Gels

		25ml	75ml
		no. of drops	
Cooling After Sun Gel*	Peppermint	2	6
	Tea Tree	10	30
	Lavender	4	12
Massage Gel for Tired & Warm Feet	Bergamot	5	15
	Tea Tree	7	21
	Peppermint	2	6
Massage Gel for Sore Muscles	Rosemary	10	30
	Lavender	10	30
	Bay Leaf	3	9
After Shave Gel	Bergamot	3	9
	Cypress	3	9
	Ylang Ylang	1	3
	Patchouli	2	6
Cellulite Gel	Grapefruit	5	15
	Cypress	5	15
	Rosemary	8	24
	Patchouli	5	15

* *good for insect bites*

Recipes for Essential Oils & Absolutes in the Home

Using Essential Oils and Absolutes to freshen up much used rooms is an excellent and pleasant way of enhancing everyday life as well as creating atmosphere for festive or special occasions.

Fragrances and blends of fragrances can be used to create a special effect: 'Romance' Blend, for that sacred time with your partner, or 'Party' Blend, to make that party of yours unforgettable. Or why not enjoy the benefit of 'Concentration' Blend when you're up late studying for your exams! Or simply use the Essential Oil you feel intuitively drawn to use at that particular time, e.g. Lavender for serenity and Bergamot for self-confidence. To freshen up your home or room, you can use an Essential Oil Fragrance Burner, a Spraying Flask or an Aroma Stone.

Essential Oil Fragrance Burner

Used for larger spaces where the effect needs to last for a while. The bigger the space, the more Oil will be required. Because Essential Oils and Absolutes evaporate spreading their aroma around the room, you may want to add more Oil after a time to maintain the effect. Top Note Oils such as Citrus and Peppermint evaporate more quickly than the Middle and Base Note Oils.

Spraying Flask

Used to create a short-term, immediate effect in a room or other space. Can be used in the car to invigorate you or to tone down the smell inside the car. When there are colds around you can spray with Lemon or Lemon Myrtle for example or after vacuuming you can use your favourite Oil or blend of Oils. Another tip is to spray covers, mattresses and pillows during airing with Lemon and Lavender to give them a clean, fresh smell.

Aroma Stones (Sand Stones)

Used to emit fragrance over a longer period of time in smaller spaces such as cupboards, toilets, halls or chests of drawers. In the car, use Peppermint to help you concentrate and at the same time counteract car-sickness. In the home or at work an Aroma Stone can be displayed as part of the décor.

Undiluted Essential Oil Drops Used Directly

In your rubbish bin or compost bucket to counteract bad odours, or put a few drops on your vacuum cleaner filter so the air being blown out is filled with the cleansing, antiseptic smell of Lemon, or apply something uplifting and stabilising like Geranium.

Table 15: Blends of Oils for Home Use

Blend	Oil	Fragrance Burner	Spary Flask 75ml
		no. of drops	no. of drops
Joy of Work	Rosemary	4	14
	Lemon	9	34
	Ylang Ylang	1	4
Party	Grapefruit	9	34
	Ylang Ylang	2	7
	Cloves	1	4
	Patchouli	2	7
Romance	Ylang Ylang	5	17
	Mandarin	6	24
	Sandalwood	3	10
Happiness	Bergamot	9	34
	Jasmine Abs*	1	2
	Ylang Ylang	1	4
Children	Lavender	4	17
	Mandarin	4	17
Tranquility	Lavender	5	17
	Ylang Ylang	3	10
	Geranium	6	24
Fitness	Orange	6	24
	Peppermint	2	8
	Rosemary	6	20
Winter Blossom	Orange	9	34
	Cloves	2	7
	Benzoin	3	10
Flowering Time	Bergamot	4	17
	Lavender	5	17
	Geranium	3	10
	Cedarwood	2	7
Sweet Dreams (An Aromantic Blend)		15	55
Exotic	Mandarin	7	24
	Ylang Ylang	3	10
	Cloves	1	4
	Benzoin	4	14
Stuffed Nose	Lemon	4	14
	Cloves	3	10
	Tea Tree	5	17
	Geranium	3	10
Heavy Head	Lavender	3	10
	Peppermint	3	10
	Rosemary	3	10
Wee Willie Winkie	Petitgrain	7	24
	Rosewood	5	17
	Vetivert	3	10
Grounding	Cypress	7	24
	Patchouli	5	17
	Vetivert	3	10
Woman	Geranium	4	14
	Rose Abs	1	3
	Vetivert	1	4
Man	Grapefruit	7	24
	Bay Leaf	5	17
	Sandalwood	5	10
Concentration Blend*	Rosemary	5	35
	Lemon	5	35

* helps with studying

Conversion Tables

Table 16 below is a quick reference conversion table between grams and millilitres.

Some customers ask how to convert grams to ml when making their Recipes. The easiest way is to invest in a sensitive gram scale. However if you don't have one, the table below shows equivalent weights and volumes for our most popular products.

Note: as an example, it is not a big difference between 2ml or 2g of Glycerine, but there's a big difference between 200ml and 200g of Glycerine. The best solution is to invest in a sensitive gram scale and to convert all of your Recipes in the future to grams. This would make for the most accurate Recipes.

Raw Materials and Colours Conversion Table

Table 16

	1g	10g	2ml	10ml
Allantoin	1.8ml	18ml	1.1g	5.5g
Beeswax in sheets	5x2 cm	10x10 cm	5x10 cm	5g
Carrageen Powder	1.3ml	13.2ml	1.5g	7.6g

	1g	10g	2ml	10ml
Cellulose	1.9ml	18.8ml	1.1g	5.3g
Cetyl-alcohol	2ml	20ml	1g	5g
Emulsifier	3ml	30.1ml	0.7g	3.3g
Glycerine Soap	0.9ml	9.2ml	2.2g	10.9g
Guar gum Powder	1.4ml	14ml	1.4g	7.1g
Hair Starch	1.6ml	15.8ml	1.3g	6.3g
Cocoa Butter Melted	1.1ml	11.2ml	1.8g	8.9g
Carbamide	1.5ml	14.7ml	1.4g	6.8g
Carnauba Wax	2.9ml	28.8ml	0.7g	3.5g
Coconut Oil Melted	1.2ml	12.4ml	1.6g	8g
Green Clay Rough	0.9ml	9.1ml	2.2g	10.9g
Green Clay Fine	2.5ml	24.8ml	0.8g	4g
Yellow Clay	1.3ml	12.7ml	1.6g	7.9g
Pink Clay	3ml	29.9ml	0.7g	3.3g
Red Clay	1.7ml	16.7ml	1.2g	6g

	1g	10g	2ml	10ml
White Clay	3.5ml	35.2ml	0.6g	2.8g
MF Emulsifier	2.5ml	25ml	0.8g	4g
Microfine Titanium Oxide	1.5ml	15ml	1.3g	6.7g
Bicarbonate of Soda	0.8ml	8ml	1.2g	12.5g
Classic Black	1.9ml	18.6ml	1.1g	5.4g
Moss Green	1.4ml	14.1ml	1.4g	7.1g
Canary Yellow	8.2ml	82ml	0.2g	1.2g
Yellow Ochre	3.8ml	38ml	0.5g	2.6g
Coffee Brown	2.1ml	21ml	1g	4.8g
Sienna Red	1.7ml	17ml	1.2g	5.8g
Ultramarine Blue	3.4ml	33.9ml	0.6g	3g

Pearlescent Colours

	1g	10g	2ml	10ml
Gold	3.4ml	33.7ml	0.6g	3g
Silver	4ml	40.2ml	0.5g	2.5g
Bordeaux Red	4ml	39.8ml	0.5g	2.5g
Bronze	4.5ml	45ml	0.4g	2.2g
Copper Red	4.7ml	47.4ml	0.4g	2.1g
Pearl White	4.9ml	49.3ml	0.4g	2g

Pearlescent Colours

	1g	10g	2ml	10ml
Blue	3.8ml	37.6ml	0.5g	2.7g
Green	1.7ml	17ml	1.2g	5.8g
Purple	3.3ml	33ml	0.6g	3g
Silk Black	4ml	40ml	0.5g	2.5g
Silk White	6.2ml	62ml	0.3g	1.5g

	1g	10g	2ml	10ml
Shea Butter Melted	1.2ml	11.8ml	1.7g	8.5g
Talc	1.8ml	18.4ml	1.1g	5.4g
VE Emulsifier	2ml	19ml	1.1g	5.3g
Vegetal	2.3ml	22.6ml	0.9g	4.4g
Xanthum Gum	2.5ml	24.6ml	0.8g	4.1g
Zinc Oxide	1.8ml	18.4ml	1.1g	5.4g

Essential Oils Conversion Table

10ml of each Essential Oil is equal to the following weights in grams.

Table 17

Vetivert	11.0g
Cloves and Cinnamon	10.5g
Myrrh	10.2g
Sandalwood	9.8g
Patchouli	9.5g
Clary Sage, Ylang Ylang	9.3g
Cedarwood Atlas	9.2g
Eucalyptus, Rosemary, Geranium	9.1g
Peppermint, Siberian Fir, Basil	9.0g
Bergamot, Lemongrass, Tea Tree	8.9g
Lavender, Neroli	8.7g
Melissa, Camphor, Lime, Mandarin, Rosewood, Black Pepper	8.6g
Lemon, Citronella, Cypress, Juniper, Grapefruit	8.5g
Orange	8.4g

Preservatives Conversion Table

Table 18

Parabens	1g = 20 drops = 0.57ml
Preservative K	1g = 34 drops = 0.93ml

Metric-US Conversion Tables

These are for our American readers and customers or those who prefer American measures. The millilitres and grams have sometimes been rounded off to make it easier for you to work with the Recipes in this book. I have used American spelling in these tables.

If you get stuck, can't see the measurement you need, or would like to be more precise in your calculations, a very useful metric conversion site with online calculators for temperature, weight and volume is www.metric-conversions.org.

Note: I use grams to weigh raw materials because it's much easier to work with and more accurate than measuring cups and spoons. This is because the volume (the space something takes up) of different raw materials will vary in relation to weight e.g. 2 ounces of Shea Butter in weight will be smaller in size (take up less volume) than 2 ounces of Dried Herbs in weight (there'll be a lot more of the Herbs i.e. it would take up more space in a measuring cup). This is why I always recommend that my students and customers buy a sensitive gram scale.

Volume (Dry)

Table 19

American Standard	Metric (millilitres)
⅛ teaspoon	0.5ml
¼ teaspoon	1ml
½ teaspoon	2ml
¾ teaspoon	4ml
1 teaspoon	5ml
1 tablespoon	15ml
¼ cup	59ml
⅓ cup	79ml
½ cup	118ml
⅔ cup	158ml
¾ cup	177ml
1 cup	225ml
2 cups or 1 pint	450ml
3 cups	675ml
4 cups or 1 quart	1 litre
½ gallon	2 litres
1 gallon	4 litres

Volume (Liquid)

Table 20

American Standard (cups & quarts)	American Standard (fluid ounces)	Metric (millilitres & litres)
⅛ teaspoon		0.5ml
¼ teaspoon		1ml
½ teaspoon		2ml
¾ teaspoon		4ml
1 teaspoon		5ml
½ tablespoon	¼ fl.oz	8ml
1 tablespoon	½ fl.oz	15ml
2 tablespoon	1 fl.oz	30ml
⅛ cup		35ml
¼ cup	2 fl.oz	65ml
⅓ cup		85ml
⅜ cup		95ml
½ cup	4 fl.oz	125ml
⅝ cup		160ml
⅔ cup		170ml
¾ cup		190ml
⅞ cup		220ml
1 cup	8 fl.oz	250ml
1½ cup	12 fl.oz	375ml
2 cups/1 pint	16 fl.oz	500ml
4 cups/1 quart	32 fl.oz	1 litre
1 gallon	128 fl.oz	4 litres

Weight/mass

Table 21

American Standard (ounces)	Metric (grams)
½ ounce	15g
1 ounce	30g
3 ounces	85g
3.75 ounces	100g
4 ounces	115g
8 ounces	225g
12 ounces	340g
16 ounces/1 lb	450g

Temperature

Table 22

Celsius (°C)	Fahrenheit (F)
10	50
15	59
20	68
25	77
30	86
35	95
40	104
45	113
50	122
60	140
65	149
70	158
75	167
80	176
85	185
90	194
95	203
100	212